CHABOT COLLEGE-HAY
2 555 000 06401

D0981992

Scientists Confront Velikovsky

Scientists Confront Velikovsky

Edited by DONALD GOLDSMITH

With a Foreword by ISAAC ASIMOV

Cornell University Press ITHACA AND LONDON

First published 1977 by Cornell University Press.
Published in the United Kingdom by Cornell University Press Ltd.,
2-4 Brook Street, London W1Y 1AA.

Second printing 1978

International Standard Book Number 0-8014-0961-6
Library of Congress Catalog Card Number 77-2457
Printed in the United States of America by Vail-Ballou Press, Inc.
Librarians: Library of Congress cataloging information appears on the last page of the book.

Contents

Foreword: The Role of the Heretic

ISAAC ASIMOV

What does one do with a heretic? We know the answer if the "one" referred to is a powerful religious orthodoxy: the heretic can be burned at the stake. If the "one" is a powerful political orthodoxy, the heretic can be sent to a concentration camp. If the "one" is a powerful socioeconomic orthodoxy, the heretic can be prevented from earning a living.

But what if the "one" is a powerful scientific orthodoxy? In that case, very little can be done, because even the most powerful scientific orthodoxy is not very powerful. To be sure, if the heretic is himself a scientist and depends on some organized scientific pursuit for his living or for his renown, things can be made hard for him. He can be deprived of government grants, of prestige-filled appointments, of access to the learned journals. This is bad enough, and not lightly to be condoned, but it is peanuts compared to the punishments that could be, and sometimes are, visited on heretics by the other orthodoxies.

Then, too, the religious, political, and socioeconomic orthodoxies can be universal in their power. A religious orthodoxy in full flight visits its punishments not on priests alone; nor a political one on politicians alone; nor a socioeconomic one on society leaders alone. No one is immune to their displeasure. The scientific orthodoxy, however, is completely helpless if the heretic is not himself a professional scientist—if he does not depend on grants or appointments, and if he places his views before the world through some medium other than the learned journals.

Therefore, if we are to consider scientific heretics, we must understand that there are two varieties with different powers and different immunities.

Let us consider the two kinds of scientific heretics: (1) There are those who arise from within the professional world of science and who are subject to punishment by the orthodoxy. We might call these heretics from within "endoheretics." (2) There are those who arise from outside the professional world of science and who are immune to direct punishment by the orthodoxy. These heretics from without are the "exoheretics."

Of the two, the endoheretics are far less well known to the general public. The endoheretic speaks in the same language as does the orthodoxy, and both views, the endoheretical and the orthodox, are equally obscure to the nonscientist, who can, generally speaking, understand neither the one nor the other nor the nature of the conflict between them.

It follows that if we consider the great endoheresies of the past, we find that the general public was not ordinarily involved. In the few cases where the public was involved, it was almost invariably on the side of the orthodoxy. The patron saint of all scientific heresies, Galileo, was, of course, an endoheretic. He was as deeply versed in Aristotelian physics and Ptolemaic astronomy, which he dethroned, as were any of his Aristotelian/Ptolemaic opponents. And since in those days and in his particular society, the scientific and religious orthodoxies were the same, Galileo had to run far greater risks than later endoheretics did. Facing the Inquisition, he had to consider the possibility, not of a canceled grant, but of physical torture. Yet we cannot suppose that there was any great popular outcry on behalf of the rebel. The general public was not concerned, nor even aware, of the dispute. Had it been made aware, it would certainly have sided with orthodoxy.

Next to Galileo, the greatest of the endoheretics was Charles Darwin, whose views on the evolution of species through the blind action of chance variation and natural selection turned biology upside down. Here, the general public *did* know of the controversy and *did*, in a very general and rough way, have a dim view of what it was about. And the public was definitely on the side of the orthodoxy. The public has remained antievolution to this day. Science has accepted Darwin without, up to this time, respectable dissent. The more sophisticated churches no longer quarrel publicly with Darwin's views. But the general public, in what is probably majority opinion if a vote were to be taken, stubbornly adheres to the tenets of a lost and dead orthodoxy of a century and a quarter ago.

Galileo and Darwin won out. Along the way, a number of the endoheretics did win. But never by public pressure. And never by a majority vote of the general public. They won out because science is a self-correcting structure, and because observation, experimentation, and reasoning eventually support those heresies which represent a more accurate view of the Universe and bury those orthodoxies which are outpaced. In the process, orthodoxy gets a bad press. Looking back on the history of science, we might suppose that every endoheretic was right—that each wore the white hat of heroism against an evil and short-sighted orthodoxy. But that is only because the history of science is naturally selective. Only the endoheretic who was, in the end, shown to be right makes his mark. For each of those, there may have been perhaps fifty endoheretics who were quite wrong, whose views are therefore scarcely remembered, and who are not recorded even as a footnote in the history books—or, if they are, it is for other, nonheretical, work.

What, then, would you have the orthodox do? Is it better to reject everything and be wrong once in fifty times—or accept everything and be wrong forty-nine out of fifty times and, in the meantime, send science down endless blind alleys? The best strategy, of course, would be neither, but to reject the forty-nine wrong out of hand and to accept and cherish the one right. Unfortunately, the day that the endoheretical pearl shines out so obviously amid the endoheretical garbage as to be easily plucked is the day of the millennium. There is, alas, no easy way of distinguishing the stroke of intuitional genius from the stroke of folly. In fact, many an utterly nonsensical suggestion has seemed to carry much more of the mark of truth than the cleverly insightful stroke of genius.

There is no way, then, of dealing with the endoheresies other than by a firm (but not blind or spiteful) opposition. Each must run the gauntlet that alone can test it.

For the self-correcting structure works. There is delay and heartbreak often enough, but it works. However grim and slow the self-questioning process of science may be (indeed, that the process exists at all is a matter of pride to scientists), science remains man's only self-correcting intellectual endeavor.

The problem of endoheresy, then, is not a truly serious one for science (though it may be, we all know, for the individual endoheretic); and the questioning process is not one which must be carried out in public.

But what of exoheresy?

We had better first be sure of what we mean by an exoheretic. Science is split into endless specialties, and a specialist who is narrow-minded and insecure may see anyone who is not bull's-eye on target within the specialty as an "outsider."

Robert Mayer was a physician and James P. Joule was a brewer who dabbled in physics. Neither had academic credentials, and, while both of them recognized the existence of the law of conservation of energy, their observations went for nothing. Neither could get his views accepted. Hermann Helmholtz, third in line, was a full academician, and he gets the credit.

When Jacobus van't Hoff worked out the scheme of the tetravalent carbon atom, the orthodox chemist Adolph Kolbe denounced the new concept intemperately, specifically and contemptuously mentioning the fact that van't Hoff was teaching at a veterinary school.

But this kind of attitude won't do. If we wish to be fine enough and narrow enough, then all scientific heretics are exoheretics in the eyes of the sufficiently orthodox, and the term becomes meaningless. Nor should we label as exoheretics those who are not formally educated but who, through self-education, have reached the peak of professional excellence. Let us, instead, understand the word exoheretic to refer only to someone who is a real outsider, one who does not understand the painstaking structure built up by science, and who therefore attacks it without understanding.

The typical exoheretic is so unaware of the intimate structure of science, of the methods and philosophy of science, of the very language of science, that his views are virtually unintelligible from the scientific standpoint. As a consequence, he is generally ignored by scientists. If exoheretical views are forced upon scientists, the reaction is bound to be puzzlement or amusement or contempt. In any case, it would be exceptional if the exoheresy were deemed worthy of any sort of comment.

In frustration, the exoheretic is very likely to appeal over the heads of the scientists to the general public. He may even be successful in this, since his inability to speak the language of science does not necessarily prevent him from speaking the language of the public. The appeal to the public is, of course, valueless from the scientific standpoint. The findings of science cannot be canceled or reversed by majority vote, or by the highest legislative or executive fiat. If every government in the world declared, officially, that the Earth is flat, and if every scientist were forbidden to argue the contrary, the Earth would nevertheless remain spheroidal, and every scrap of evidence maintaining that conclusion would still exist.

Nevertheless, the appeal to the public has other rewards than that of establishing scientific proof. (1) A favorable public response is soul-satisfying. The exoheretic can easily convince himself that his position at the center of a cult demonstrates the value of his views. He can easily argue himself into believing that people would not flock to nonsense, though all history shows otherwise. (2) A favorable public response can be lucrative. It is well known that books and lectures dealing favorably with a popular cult do far better than do books and lectures debunking it, even when the books in favor may be poorly written and reasoned, whereas the books against may be models of lucidity and rationality. (3) A favorable public response may hound scientists into open opposition, and they may express, with injudicious force, their opinion of the obvious nonsense of the exoheretical views. This very opposition, casting the exoheretic into the role of martyr, works to accentuate the first two advantages.

Public support or no, the exoheretic virtually never proves to be right. (How can he be right when he, quite literally, doesn't know what he's talking about?) Of course, he may prove to have said something somewhere in his flood of words that bears some resemblance to something that later proves to be so, and this coincidental concurrence of word and fact may be hailed by his followers as proving all the rest of the corpus of his work. This outcome, however, has only cultic value.

We see, then, the vast difference between the effects of the views of endoheretics and exoheretics. First, the public is generally not interested in the endoheretic, or, if aware of him at all, is hostile to him. The endoheretic therefore rarely profits from his heresy in any material way.* The public, on the other hand, can be very interested in the exoheretic and can support him with a partisan and even religious fervor, so that the exoheretic may, in a material way, profit very considerably by his heresy.

Second, the endoheretic is sometimes right, and since startling scientific advances usually begin as heresies, some of the greatest names in science have been endoheretics. The exoheretic, on the other hand, is virtually never right, and the history of science contains no great advance, to my knowledge, initiated by an exoheretic.

One might combine these generalizations and, working backward (not always a safe procedure), state that when a view denounced by scientists as false is, nevertheless, popular with the general public, the mere fact of that popularity is strong evidence in favor of its worthlessness. It is on the basis of public popularity of particular beliefs, for instance, that I, even without personal investigation of such matters, feel it safe to be ex-

* I must qualify these generalizations because there are exceptions, of course. Edward Jenner, who advanced the endoheretical technique of smallpox vaccination, was accepted eagerly by the public, and profited materially as a result.

tremely skeptical about ancient astronauts, or about modern astronauts in UFO's, or about the value of talking to plants, or about psi phenomena, or about spiritualism, or about astrology.*

And this brings me to Velikovskianism at last.

Of all the exoheretics, Velikovsky has come closest to discomfiting the science he has attacked, and has most successfully forced science to take him seriously. Why is that? Well——

(1) Velikovsky has been a psychiatrist, so that he has training in a scientific specialty of sorts and is not an utter exoheretic. What's more, he has the faculty of sounding as though he knows what he is talking about when he invades the precincts of astronomy. He doesn't make very many elementary mistakes, and he is able to use the language of science sufficiently well to impress a layman.

(2) He is an interesting writer. It's fun to read his books. I have read every book he has published and hope to read any he writes in the future. Although he doesn't lure me into accepting his views, I can well see where those less knowledgeable in the fields Velikovsky deals with would succumb.

(3) Velikovsky's views in *Worlds in Collision* are designed to demonstrate that the Bible has a great deal of literal truth in it, that the miraculous events described in the Old Testament really happened as described. To be sure, Velikovsky abandons the hypothesis that divine intervention caused the miracles and substitutes a far less satisfactory hypothesis involving planetary Ping-Pong, but that scarcely alters the fact that in our theistic society any claimed finding that tends to demonstrate the truth of the Bible is highly likely to meet with general favor.

These three points are enough in themselves to explain Velikovsky's popularity. Supply the public with something amusing, that sounds scholarly, and that supports an idea it wants to believe, and surely you need nothing more. Erich von Daniken and his theories of ancient astronauts have succeeded on little

* Of course, I would also have used this line of reasoning to feel it safe to be skeptical about the value of smallpox vaccination, but the facts would have converted me within a year in that case.

more than this, even though his books are less amusing than Velikovsky's, sound less scholarly, and support something less substantial than belief in the Bible.

Velikovsky, however, has succeeded beyond such popularity. Because of the climate of the times when *Worlds in Collision* was published, there was an astronomical overreaction. The appearance of excerpts from his book, prior to publication, in *Harper's*, *Reader's Digest*, and *Collier's*, and the widespread publicity given to his views, goaded some astronomers into an attempt at censorship. To paraphrase Fouché, this was worse than immoral; it was a blunder.

The fact that Velikovsky could then portray himself as a persecuted martyr has cast a Galilean glow upon all his endeavors, and has canceled out any attempt on the part of astronomers to demonstrate, clearly and dispassionately, the errors in the Velikovskian view. All attempts in this direction can be (and are) dismissed as persecution.

It also gives a glow of heroism to Velikovsky's followers. They can attack an orthodoxy—ordinarily such attacks are accepted as courageous—and can do so with complete safety, since in actual fact (as opposed to Velikovskian fantasy) the orthodoxy does not, and indeed cannot, strike back.

From the standpoint of science, is Velikovskianism nothing but an irritation and a waste of time? Not at all. It has enormous benefits. For one thing, Velikovskianism, and indeed, any exoheretical view that becomes prominent enough to force itself on science, acts to puncture scientific complacency—and that is good. An exoheresy may cause scientists to bestir themselves for the purpose of re-examining the bases of their beliefs, even if only to gather firm and logical reasons for the rejection of the exoheresy—and that is good, too. An exoheresy may cause scientific activity which, in serendipitous fashion, may uncover something worthwhile that has nothing to do with the exoheresy—and that is very good, if it happens. The Fates keep science from remaining unchallenged. Science is in far greater danger from the absence of challenge than from the coming of any number of even absurd challenges.

At the American Association for the Advancement of Science meeting in 1974, scientists as a group responded to Velikovsky's exoheretical challenge for the first time. Four of the five essays in this book were prepared for and read at that meeting for other scientists and are now published in slightly revised form for the general public. For reasons explained in Donald Goldsmith's Introduction, the papers by Velikovsky and Irving Michelson do not appear in this book.

It was altogether fitting and proper that Velikovsky and his opponents agreed to hold this discussion at the AAAS meetings. Though one could be sure from the start that nothing scientists could say would in the least move the Velikovskians, and that no amount of mere logic would shake their faith, it was still a good thing—for science.

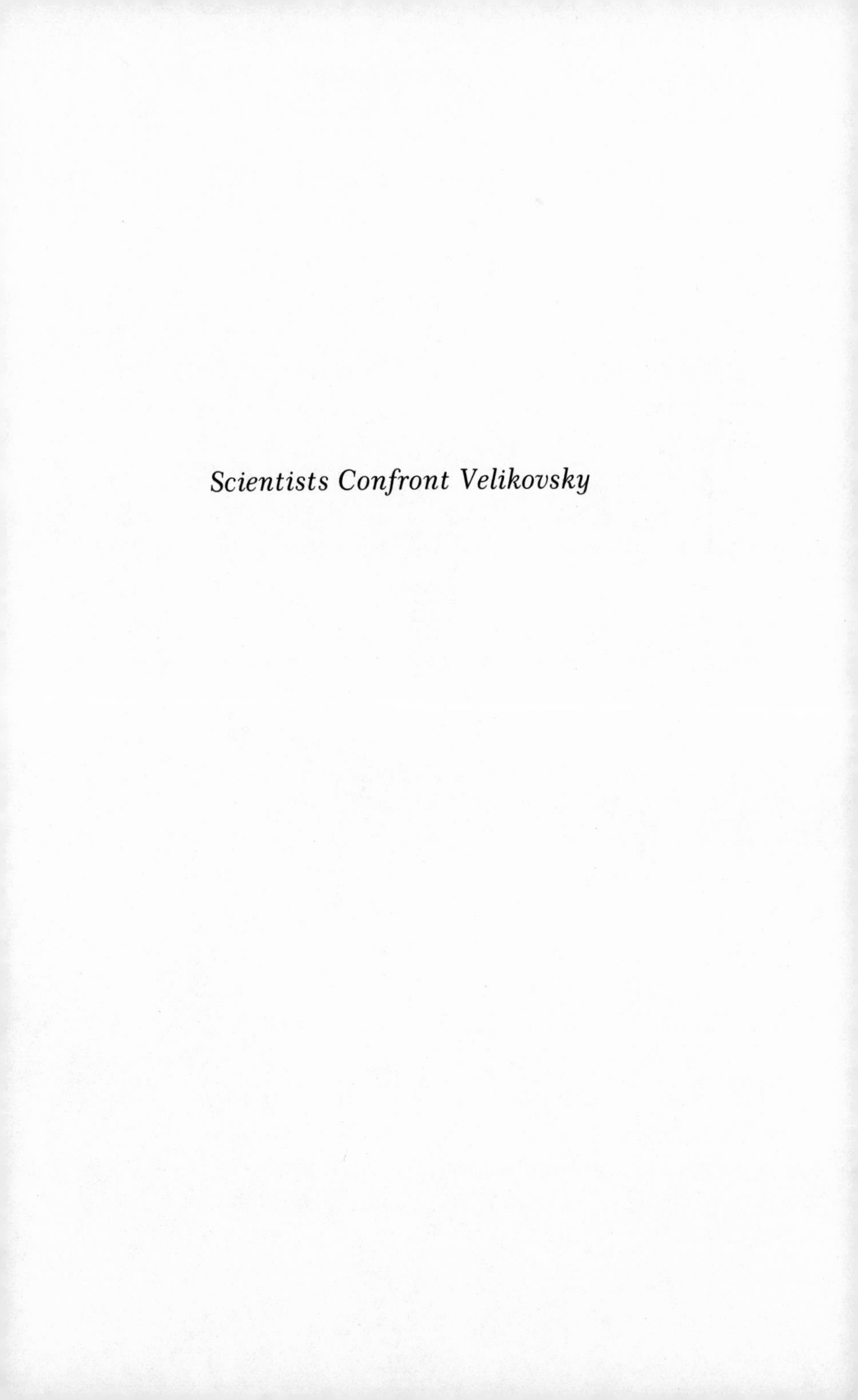

Scientists Confront Velikovsky

Introduction

DONALD GOLDSMITH

The year 1950 was a poor one for dissenting thought in the United States. Following hard on the heels of 1949, when the Soviet Union first exploded an atomic bomb, when China was "lost" by Chiang Kai-shek, and when Alger Hiss was convicted of perjury, 1950 opened with the assertion by Senator Joseph McCarthy that the U.S. State Department contained 205 employees who were security risks and 57 who were, or had been, or might have been, Communists. In June of 1950, Communist forces crossed the 38th parallel in Korea to begin a war that lasted three years and divided Korea for at least the next generation. The United States, securely placed as the world's premier power a short time before, now appeared threatened on all sides from abroad and by deviant forces and personalities from within. For two years Senator McCarthy and his followers struck at the rights of citizens to think as they chose, and the rippling effects of their actions have lasted to the present time.

The year 1950 also brought the publication of *Worlds in Collision,* the first of a series of books by Dr. Immanuel Velikovsky, a Russian-born doctor of medicine who had lived in the United States since 1939. For ten years Velikovsky had developed his theory that the Biblical account of the Israelites' flight from Egypt some three millennia ago carries the record of great natural catastrophes. Velikovsky had become convinced that these catastrophes arose from close encounters of Venus with the planet Earth during a time when Venus, ejected from the planet Jupiter, had not yet settled into its present, almost circular, orbit around the sun. These ideas, as formulated and elucidated by Velikovsky, grew into a long and complex book, to be followed eventually by three additional works (*Ages in Chaos* [1952], *Earth in Upheaval* [1955], and *Oedipus and Akhnaton* [1960]). To this corpus of Velikovskian thought, Velikovsky's admirers have added a much larger body of books and articles.

In January 1950 *Harper's* provided a favorable prepublication review of the first book in the series in the form of an article by Eric Larrabee, but in its March, 1950, issue printed a number of highly critical letters in response to the review and to Velikovsky's contentions. Biting reviews appeared also in *Science News Letter* (February 25, March 25, and April 15), and in *The Reporter* (March 14). Respected scientists criticized Velikovsky's theories and Macmillan's role in making them available. Macmillan published *Worlds in Collision* on April 3, 1950, and sold some 55,000 copies before transferring its rights to Doubleday in June, 1950.

The reaction of astronomers, archaeologists, and historians to Velikovsky's work was then and has continued to be overwhelmingly negative. However, the fury of the initial attacks on Velikovsky's ideas, which in my opinion arose in part because scientists and intellectuals generally felt themselves to be under attack in 1950, have diminished with the years to surly expressions of distaste, voiced by both sides. The attractiveness of Velikovsky's theories to the general public diminished during the late 1950's and early 1960's, perhaps because the public had become sated with catastrophism, but with the arrival of a new generation of readers and a better climate for unconventional thought, a modest boom in Velikovskian views started around 1968 and reached its crest, perhaps, in 1974. By this time Velikovsky had become the grand curmudgeon of antiestablishment science, a man who had spent thirty years or more in opposition to most of the fundamental notions of astronomy (one of Velikovsky's first papers argued against the validity of Newton's law of gravitation).[1] Younger readers of Velikovsky's works began to speak out in favor of his ideas, and with time a small Velikovsky industry crystallized around the nucleus of the "Student Academic Freedom Forum" in Portland, Oregon, which published ten issues of a journal called *Pensée* (1972 to 1974) that were entirely devoted to supporting Velikovsky's theories.

The twenty-five-year history of the Velikovskian collision with the scientific world provides an interesting example of the relationship between established scientific theorists (and their theories) and those persons who seek to establish theories that contradict the conventional view. Both parties to the Velikovskian dispute have sought to uphold the importance of the "scientific" approach to debate, one in which logic rules and passions remain subordinate to reasoned argument. But difficulties arise when the logical truth of one side's argument fails to receive acceptance by the other, leaving passion in the van and courtesy far behind. Both sides remain committed to the significance of the new ideas under debate—one because they represent a lifetime of effort, the other because acceptance of the idea would require a wholesale reorganization of the way in which we regard the solar system and, by extension, all of celestial mechanics. Velikovsky's ideas would be of the utmost importance if they were correct: well-established concepts in a host of disciplines would then fall like leaves in the wind.

Although many astronomers have met Velikovsky's theories with abhorrence and scorn, their refusal to treat Velikovskian ideas as worthy of serious debate has underscored the size of the idols that Velikovsky has tried to overturn. He has not only attacked established theories, he has also done so from outside the accepted bounds of expertise. Norman Storer points out in his contribution to this volume, as does Isaac Asimov in the Foreword, that scientists typically do not respond to ideas that come from outside the established framework of participants. Thus, for example, Alfred Wegener's theories of continental drift aroused the contumely of geologists for decades, mostly because Wegener was trained as a meteorologist.

But not every idea that arises outside the scientific establishment eventually proves to be acceptable, as Wegener's has. In fact, and not surprisingly in view of human fallibility, most such ideas are wrong, as indeed most new theories proposed within a given discipline of science turn out to be partly or wholly flawed. Scientists have formed a guild with well-defined rules of entry. Those who try to come in through the wrong door are typically treated as gate-crashers at a fashionable party: first with disdain, then with open hostility. To many scientists, Velikovsky's lack of credentials, together with his rise to prominence in the public consciousness, placed him on a par with the *nouveaux riches* at a gathering of the Cabots and Lowells. The analogy extends to the manner in which social groups consider "high society" as a club well worth joining, and the harder the "ins" bar the door, the more the "outs," for all their invective against the misguided exclusivity of social divisions, seek entry. The aggrieved tone of the Velikovsky supporters who see their ideas barred from establishment acceptance appears in a quotation (and a representative one) from *Pensée:*

> [Carl] Sagan . . . contended that "where Velikovsky is original he is very likely wrong; and that where he is right the idea has been preempted by earlier workers. There are also a large number of cases . . . where he is neither right nor original." This statement . . . is flatly untrue, and Sagan did not attempt to document his claim. Such an effort to discredit another scholar's work is highly unethical, and deserves investigation by the official AAAS committee on ethics.[2]

The American Association for the Advancement of Science (AAAS) has not responded to this challenge. I would guess that investigations by the bushel would be needed to probe into all accusations of "untrue" statements made by one scientist about another's theories. Readers of Sagan's contribution in this volume can decide whether or not he has fairly documented his claim.

How did the AAAS come to be charged with overlooking a breach of ethics? The statement by Sagan quoted above was made at a symposium on Velikovsky's theories held on February 25, 1974, during the annual meeting of the AAAS in San Francisco. This symposium, the first one dealing with Velikovsky's work to be sponsored by an "establishment" scientific organization, owed its inception to Carl Sagan, the man accused of untruth by *Pensée*. Sagan has become well known as an astronomer who writes and speaks in a way that nonscientists can understand; in this, he represents an exception among scientists, one who enjoys communicating with people and who has been unafraid of the snickers of his more reserved colleagues for appearing on television, collaborating on movie scripts, and writing books that have no footnotes and sell well.

Sagan had long maintained that the stated commitment of the AAAS to the sharing of scientific ideas with the public, together with the public interest in Velikovsky's theories, provided sufficient reason to hold a symposium at one of its general meetings, whatever scientists might think of the merit of Velikovsky's ideas. These sentiments were shared by Walter Orr Roberts, a past president of the AAAS, and in 1972 Sagan and Roberts managed to convince both Ivan King and Owen Gingerich (respectively the chairmen of the AAAS sections on astronomy and the history and philosophy of science for 1973) of the validity of their proposal. In addition, Sagan convinced me—but that was easy, since I had been Sagan's student during my undergraduate years at Harvard College.

Incidentally, it is worth noting (and to Velikovsky's supporters, it is definitive proof of a cabal against Velikovsky) that much of the opposition to Velikovsky's work has had a Harvard connection. Harlow Shapley and Cecilia Payne-Gaposchkin, two of Velikovsky's early detractors, were both Harvard professors. King was a graduate student at Harvard, Gingerich both a graduate student and a professor, and Sagan was an assistant professor there for four years. Much of this linkage is related to Harvard's reputation as having one of the outstanding astronomy research centers in the United States for the past hundred years.

At any rate, by 1973, when the AAAS had committed itself to holding a symposium on Velikovsky's work, King was a professor at the University of California at Berkeley, Sagan was a professor at Cornell University, and I was an assistant professor at the State University of New York at Stony Brook. My position there left me ample time to help with the details of arranging the symposium, and I was chosen to be a co-organizer along with King and Gingerich.

All three of us knew that we faced some ticklish moments. For one thing, Velikovsky had been spurned and disliked by much of the astronomical community for a generation, and he had come to see the scientific world as an anti-Velikovsky league. For another, many scientists and many nonscientists would consider holding a symposium on Velikovsky's theories to be an admission that these theories must have some validity. I did not, and do not, share this view; still I considered it quite likely to be widespread, and was willing to risk criticism. The precedent that I kept in mind was an AAAS symposium on Unidentified Flying Objects (UFO's), organized by Carl Sagan and Thornton Page. Meeting in 1969, this symposium had brought together some of those who believe UFO's to be definitely established as sent by extraterrestrial beings of great intelligence, as well as some who believe that all UFO reports can be explained by science or result from trickery. The published proceedings (*UFO's—A Scientific Debate,* Cornell University Press, 1972) provide a valuable point of departure for anyone who wishes to approach the question with a partly open mind. If astronomy, and the AAAS, could withstand a symposium on UFO's, we felt sure that they could bear one on Velikovsky; and if some people assume that these symposia are proof that UFO's are indeed extraterrestrial and that Velikovsky's theories are correct, society could bear this too. As it turned out, the symposium was held, Velikovsky and other speakers stated their views, and the world went on much as before.

Not, however, without a large amount of local disturbance. In July, 1973, King visited Velikovsky, invited him to participate in the symposium, and received his acceptance. We three organizers located Norman Storer, a sociologist of science, to discuss the reaction of the scientific community, and also asked Peter Huber at the Eidgenössische Technische Hochschule in Zurich to examine Velikovsky's treatment of ancient observations of Venus. In addition, we arranged for Derral Mulholland (of the

University of Texas) to consider Velikovsky's celestial mechanics, and for Carl Sagan to discuss Velikovsky's theories of planetary astronomy. We looked for a physicist who favored Velikovsky's ideas, and located Irving Michelson of the Illinois Institute of Technology, who said that although he did not agree with all of Velikovsky's theories, he was basically sympathetic. With these six panelists we had a program, and at this point the fun began in earnest.

First, I began to hear from one after the other of those who had something to say about Velikovsky's ideas, pro and con—each of them convinced that his or her contribution was essential to the discussion we had arranged. This eagerness to participate assured me that public interest was high, and I pointed out time and again that the morning session which the AAAS had allotted us was already filled (indeed, as it turned out, overfilled) by the six speakers already invited. Eventually, we had to arrange an evening session, to which I invited everyone to come and speak out; many did just that.

Second, we began to learn that some scientists continued to oppose holding any symposium on Velikovsky under the aegis of the AAAS. This opposition, based almost entirely on the premise that the public would equate a pro-and-con symposium with uncritical acceptance of Velikovsky's theories, seemed to me overfearful and also totally opposed to the spirit (sadly battered in practice) of scientific inquiry. My chest began to swell with pride over my willingness to proceed despite opprobrium as I read letters that spoke of "producing more confusion than public understanding," or of "no productive interaction." One astronomer wrote that "scientists only get a bloody nose when they attempt to tangle with popular mysticism." Figuratively clutching my streaming proboscis, I was cheered to see that scientists continued to behave in their usual ways. For example, the writers quoted above had expressed themselves, as is natural in the hierarchy, not to Gingerich, to King, or to me, but to the president of the AAAS, Roger Revelle. Revelle in his turn knew how to reassure his correspondents—with the credentials of the organizers—saying "although I cannot find out who

Goldsmith is, Gingerich and King seem to me to be respectable figures in the history of science and astronomy." This apparently sufficed, and we carried our respectability onward to San Francisco.

The symposium itself turned out to be the best attended, and the most widely reported, of the hundreds held at the AAAS meeting. It is hard to outdo the spectacle of a seventy-seven-year-old gentleman rising to confront the critics who had rejected him for scores of years, with his supporters in the audience cheering his wit and hissing at his opponents, while his detractors sat applauding and protesting in opposite phase. Readers of *Pensée* can discover how the day appeared to those who favored Velikovsky's position, and can read the record of "errors" made by those reporters who considered Velikovsky to be routed, or even daunted, by his opponents. Most of the reporters, and indeed most of the audience, saw the debate as a direct confrontation between Sagan and Velikovsky, the sort of convenient simplification that our experience with televised sports events has led us to expect, and that makes for easier coverage in the press. Only a few reporters commented on the quasi-religious tone of the Velikovsky-Sagan exchanges, in which a patriarch, whose work aims, among other things, at restoring the importance and the truth of the Biblical account of the Exodus, faced a representative of a later generation of Jewish scholars, one who had (from Velikovsky's viewpoint) turned away from the literal truth of the Bible in favor of a more modern account of the history of the solar system.

The evening session that followed the morning's five presentations (Michelson's talk had to be postponed until evening because the speakers, especially Velikovsky, ran overtime) brought a fascinating array of talent to the microphones of the St. Francis Hotel's California West Ballroom. In addition to those who had well-reasoned, if often long-winded, polemics for or against Velikovsky's ideas, I remember in particular a man who claimed to be in direct contact with the genius Charles Steinmetz (who died in 1923), and a woman who had made many trips to faraway solar systems. Several speakers warmed my heart by expressing their delight that such a symposium had occurred at all, whether or not Velikovsky's theories proved to be correct. We three organizers left the symposium exhausted but satisfied: We had succeeded in presenting a symposium on Velikovsky's ideas without destroying either the fabric of science or our own careers. Now all that remained was to arrange for publication of the symposium proceedings, so that interested parties could use the discussions as a means of examining Velikovsky's approach.

Here, however, a protracted difficulty arose from Velikovsky's objections to the proposed publication. As editor of the symposium volume, I was anxious that all six contributions be included, but obtaining agreement proved to be impossible. Velikovsky insisted on writing a supplement to his paper, pointing out that since Sagan's contribution was longer than his oral presentation (Sagan had skipped through the written version to save time), he (Velikovsky) should have additional space for rebuttal. Eventually an upper limit of 6,000 words was set on this supplement, which seemed to be acceptable, but despite this apparent agreement, Velikovsky did not submit his contribution on time even though the deadline was extended twice. Michelson also did not agree to have his contribution included in this volume.

The editors of Cornell University Press and I felt that the four remaining contributions to the Velikovsky symposium deserved to be published. In addition, David Morrison was invited to submit an article he had prepared on planetary astronomy, a paper that was not presented at the AAAS symposium. Isaac Asimov, the well-known science writer, was asked to provide a prefatory piece giving his perspective on the turmoil surrounding Velikovsky's views. Here, in a full-scale critique, Velikovsky's theories are confronted by the insight and intelligence of a group of notable scientists that includes three astronomers, a sociologist, and an expert on ancient astronomical records. The book not only shows the deficiencies of Velikovsky's views, but also explains why these views have attracted so much attention for more than a quarter of a century.

Had we been able to publish all of the symposium papers in one volume, the title "World Views in Collision" would have been most appropriate. As it is, the colliding views can be seen here only from the side of those who do not subscribe to Velikovsky's theories, but this is not a bad place to start. The pro-Velikovsky side can be best found in *Pensée,* where Velikovsky's and Michelson's papers were published in late 1974, and in *Velikovsky Reconsidered.*[3] To me it is symbolically appropriate that the collision of Velikovsky and his supporters with some of his detractors did not produce any mutual adhesion. Despite their common respect for the importance of astronomy, there remains a wide gulf between the Velikovskian picture of worlds in collision and the established view of noncolliding planets moving in near-circular orbits for millions or billions of years. I, however, have gained a world of experience from the collision, and am pleased that a record of at least part of the symposium has now become available to the reading public.

In editing the contributions presented in this volume, I have made changes only in the interest of greater readability. These changes are basically minor ones and consist of the elimination of some technical details and the addition of a few phrases and sentences of explanation. Carl Sagan has slightly expanded and revised his contribution, but his ten objections to Velikovsky's theories remain the same ten he presented at the AAAS meeting in San Francisco.

Notes

1. Immanuel Velikovsky, "Cosmos without Gravitation," Scientific Report IV of the *Scripta Academica Hierosolymitana* (New York-Jersulalem: Simon Velikovsky Foundation, 1946).
2. *Pensée* 4:41–42, 1974.
3. *Velikovsky Reconsidered* (New York: Doubleday, 1976). This selection of papers originally published in *Pensée* does not include the talks given by Velikovsky and by Michelson in San Francisco; these appear in *Pensée* 4:10–21, 1974.

1 The Sociological Context of the Velikovsky Controversy

NORMAN W. STORER

My task here is to set the topic in its broad sociological framework, hoping thereby to bring to the controversy a sense of perspective that can mute passions and facilitate rationality. I should admit at the outset that I am quite unable to arrive at defensible conclusions regarding competing theories of the Earth's history. Instead, my expertise, such as it is, lies in a very different area. The sociological study of science and scientists has been my specialty for the past fifteen years, and while I am a layman when it comes to comets and catastrophes, or fossils and folktales, I believe that what my colleagues and I have discovered about the behavior of scientists will be relevant to the discussion presented in this volume.

To provide some sociological perspective on the topic, let us begin with a sketch of science as a community, or as a coherent social system. We may assume that it *is* a coherent community not only because it is clearly distinguished from other sectors of society, but because its principal product—organized, certified empirical knowledge—requires a particular form of continuing cooperation among those who make up its membership. What, then, are the distinguishing qualities of the group of people, numbering in the hundreds of thousands and yet geographically dispersed, who make up this community?

The Scientific Community

Basically, scientists must be characterized by a distinctive set of interrelationships. This is not to say that a person identified as a scientist will behave differently twenty-four hours a day from a person identified as a banker, for the word "scientist" identifies social position rather than a concrete human being. Just as a person will behave differently toward others when at work as a banker than when at home as a parent, so someone identified as a scientist will behave as a scientist only in certain situations. What we are talking about, then, is the relationships among a set of social positions rather than the relationships among a number of physical human beings. This point will take on added meaning later.

We assume that the distinctive relationships found among a set of people occupying certain social positions are due to their sharing a set of norms—standards of proper behavior—that tell them how to behave with respect to each other. Thanks to the work of Robert K. Merton,[1] we have a pretty clear idea of what these norms are for scientists, although the names sociologists give to the norms may be unfamiliar.

The Norms of Science. Merton identifies four norms that are central to the ethos of science. First, there is *universalism*—implementing the principle that the truth of a scientific statement is totally divorced from the personal characteristics of the person who makes it. A statement about the Earth's electromagnetic field is true or false on grounds totally unrelated to the speaker's ethnicity, sex, creed, or personal idiosyncracies, and a scientist should ignore such things when evaluating the statement.

Second, there is *communality*—the requirement that a scientist's findings should be shared freely with others. We know, for instance, that a scientist who is excessively secretive will be subject to censure, and that classified research is anathema to scientists. The desire to publish, in other words, is not simply a sign of egotism or of selfish ambition; the scientist is morally obliged to try to share what he or she has discovered.

Third, we have the norm of *organized skepticism.* In effect, this encourages scientists to scrutinize their colleagues' contributions critically and to make their criticisms known. Without such mutual policing of each other's attempts to add to a body of knowledge, the archives of science would be filled with erroneous data and unfounded speculations, and the organized, cumulative character of scientific knowledge would be seriously undermined. We do not publicly question another scientist's conclusions simply because we are combative; we do it because it would be a sin of omission *not* to point out errors we believe we have found. And so we have referees, critical reviews, arguments in the letter columns of our journals—and a well-reinforced desire in each of us to make sure that what *we* publish will be as valid and unassailable as possible.

Finally, there is the norm of *disinterestedness,* or the stricture that a scientist's research should not be guided by hope of personal reward. One should be a "pure" scientist, following knowledge for its own sake rather than consciously designing one's research in order to maximize private economic gain, glory in the eyes of the layman, or even the plaudits of one's colleagues. It is the apparent violation of this norm by applied researchers, for instance, that seems to account for the invidious distinction often made between basic and applied science. Basic is "better," because it is free to follow wherever the demands of developing knowledge lead, rather than being directed by the interests of a lay employer who pays one's salary.

Together, these four norms lay out a kind of blueprint for the relationships of scientists to each other, and thus describe a social structure.

Professional Recognition. Let me go on now to introduce the "energy" that seems to animate this structure, or to drive the engine of science. This energizing force—again, we know this through the work of Merton—is the scientist's interest in acquiring professional recognition.

Professional recognition, the public acknowledgment by one's peers that one's work has been significant in advancing knowledge, is the only "property right" one may have in it, given the norm of communality. To have a law, or a species, or a technique named for one, or even to be footnoted occasionally, is to receive professional recognition. Intrinsically gratifying, as well as being sometimes of utilitarian value, recognition publicly bestowed by one's peers is thus the institutionally appropriate reward for successful performance as a scientist. Contests over priority in discovery (since priority is necessary if one is to receive credit for a discovery) attest to the value scientists have placed on professional recognition for the past five hundred years. Galileo excoriated those who would claim credit for his discoveries, and the entire drama of James D. Watson's *The Double Helix* rests on the significance, to all concerned, of the Nobel Prize—the prize being perhaps the highest form of professional recognition a living scientist may receive.

Organized Knowledge. To conclude this discussion of the scientific community, let me point out that the content of scientific interaction, and thus the norms that guide it and the energy that inspires it, has little meaning if it does not have reference to an organized body of knowledge. Without a significant degree of consensus regarding what is already known, so that scientists can agree on the identification of important problems as well as standards of acceptable communication and criteria of proof, professional recognition loses all meaning, and the norms of science have no purpose. In other words, as Thomas Kuhn[2] pointed out more than a decade ago, the orderly work of science is founded on the existence of a shared paradigm that provides the universe of discourse within which scientists can interact meaningfully in extending a body of empirical knowledge.

The existence of a reasonably well-organized universe of discourse, however, is important beyond these "technical" grounds. To be a scientist is not only to do what scientists do, but to accept what other scientists accept—especially the paradigms that one's predecessors and colleagues have built. A thoroughly professionalized scientist depends on this universe of discourse for an important part of his or her identity. To be a scientist is to be a part of the company that has constructed and is continuing to extend an intricately interlocking body of statements about some aspect of physical reality.

The Pathologies of Science

With both structure and energy, together with the foundation that gives them meaning, described now in paradigmatic form, we have an ideal model of the scientific community. Let me stress that it is *ideal,* for it no more describes what scientists actually do than religious teachings describe the actual behavior of those who claim to accept them. Yet ideals do shape human behavior, and we can say that those who occupy the social position of "scientist" feel a strong obligation to obey the norms of science as best they can. Under normal circumstances, we can assume that most of them, most of the time, obey the norms reasonably well.

But what about departures from these norms? What do we know about violations of the norms of science? While behavioral departures from normative standards may be deplorable, they are also to be expected, and an important task of the sociologist is to discover the reasons for patterned evasions of norms. He or she usually finds that these can be accounted for as the outcome of attempts to compromise between two conflicting norms, or because it is humanly impossible fully to obey the dictates of a single norm, or because the people involved do not accept the relevance of a norm to their behavior in a particular situation.

Let me briefly illustrate each of these deviance-generating circumstances in science, and then turn to an analysis of the Velikovsky affair in terms of the perspective developed thus far.

Conflict between Norms. There is, for example, potential conflict between the norm of communality and the institutionally reinforced desire to earn professional recognition. To share one's hunches or one's preliminary findings too early might give someone else a chance to solve a problem first, so that one would lose the opportunity to achieve priority. Yet the norm of communality seems to call for full disclosure without specifying any circumstances to which it is inapplicable. The result is moral conflict—and the emergence of patterns of temporary secrecy which may justly be viewed by others as violations of the norm.

Inability to Obey a Single Norm. In the case of a single norm, consider the human impossibility of obeying completely the norm of organized skepticism. Who among us has the time, energy, or facilities to respond critically to *every* contribution to our field? Graduate students become rightly indignant when they receive little or no substantive response to their papers, or when response is delayed overly long; scientists sense that they have been morally wronged when their books are not reviewed or when colleagues do not respond to their preprints. Although we are aware that we may be subject to criticism for failing to respond promptly and fully to each contribution we receive, we accept our vulnerability because it is humanly impossible for us to obey the norm completely. The actual criteria we use in deciding which contributions deserve serious response often involve personal relationships, status considerations, and similar factors which ought, ideally, to be irrelevant to the matter—and thus involve us covertly in patterned evasions of the norm.

Irrelevant Norms. Finally, let us remember that institutional norms are generally taken to govern the relationships among the social positions that make up an institution. The norms of science, in other words, govern the relationships among people *in their roles as scientists;* they are not necessarily relevant to these people's behavior when they are occupying different social positions or when, as scientists, they are interacting with nonscientists. As a married person, a scientist does not feel it necessary to respond critically to everything his or her spouse says: the norm of organized skepticism is clearly inappropriate to this relationship. A scientist does not share his or her private foibles with everyone who asks, for the norm of communality does not cover our nonscientific activities or govern our relationships with curious strangers.

But even when we are placed in the role of scientist by someone else, as when the author of a flat-earth tract addresses it to us at the observatory, we do not feel it incumbent upon us to accept the norms of science as governing our relationship to this person. To obey the norm of organized skepticism here would call for a lengthy reply which, if adequate, would constitute a fairly thorough introduction to the history and current state of astronomy. Scientists have all received such "contributions to knowledge," and I imagine not a few of us have files marked "Crackpot" into which such things go without being answered at all. Who among us has the time to handle such things any other way—and why should we? The norms of science are clearly inoperative in such situations.

The Velikovsky Controversy

In order to bring the foregoing analysis of science to bear upon the Velikovsky controversy, let us review briefly the history of his work. According to Alfred de Grazia,[3] editor of the 1966 volume entitled *The Velikovsky Affair*, Velikovsky received his medical diploma in 1921 from the University of Moscow, stayed for a while in Berlin, and moved to Palestine in 1924, where he practiced medicine (and later psychoanalysis) for fifteen years. During a visit to New York in 1939 to 1940, "he chanced upon an idea that was to completely alter his life plans and keep him in America for decades" (de Grazia, p. 13). This was the idea that ancient histories and myths not only may contain more truth than we have supposed, but that correlations among them may help us to discover the true prehistory of the Earth.

An early draft of *Ages in Chaos* was finished in 1942 (New York: Doubleday, 1952), and by 1946 Velikovsky had developed the major theses of what was to appear later as *Worlds in Collision* (New York: Doubleday, 1950; in paperback: Dell Books, 1967). There followed several attempts to persuade scientists to obtain or develop data that would test these hypotheses, but either the necessary instrumentation did not then exist or the scientists to whom he addressed his requests declined to cooperate. During the same period, Velikovsky sought a publisher for *Worlds in Collision* and signed an optional contract with the Macmillan Company in May, 1947. A final contract was signed in late 1948 or early 1949 after "various outside readers [had] examined the manuscript and recommended publication" (de Grazia, p. 19), and the book was eventually published in 1950.

Public notice first came through the lead article in the January 1950 issue of *Harper's*, and that was quickly followed by other articles in *Reader's Digest* and *Collier's*. Critical response came almost immediately from scientists, both in general magazines and in scientific journals. The history of the controversy since 1950 is well enough known to make it unnecessary for me to go into further detail here.

The analyses by de Grazia and others of how the scientific establishment responded to Velikovsky's assertions seem amply to document charges that in certain cases both the norms of science and the norms of common courtesy were violated. Indeed, the affair has become a classic case study used to flay "scientism" for its hypocrisy and its self-serving censorship of ideas that threaten established scientific dogma.

The Scientific Community under Attack. If we are to stick to a sociological perspective, viewing science as a community, we must pay attention also to its social environment. I suggest that this environment during the late 1940's and early 1950's was particularly important in shaping the community's response to Velikovsky. During this period, science and indeed all intellectual enterprise seemed to be under attack by right-wing forces in American society. The Cold War was at its chilliest, Congress was obsessed with atomic secrets, and Senator Joseph McCarthy was waiting in the wings. Blacklists were drawn up, loyalty oaths were required, and to be a scientist was to be a potential traitor; the Oppenheimer Hearings in 1954 were perhaps the culmination of this growing national paranoia.

Scientists quickly adopted a defensive posture, and one could hardly expect them to welcome with open arms another apparent attempt to discredit established scientific knowledge. If we add to this the fact that Velikovsky could be only marginally distinguished then from the myriad of eccentrics who have always assailed science, perhaps the initial response to his work can be understood.

Velikovsky as an Outsider. It was clear, for instance, that Velikovsky did not possess credentials that would have signaled scientists that the ordinary norms of science should govern their relationships with him. There could be little doubt that he was a scholar, but his professional background could not support their granting him full-fledged membership in the scientific community.

His ideas seemed obviously in conflict with accepted physical facts and laws, and his failure to show how these apparently logical inconsistencies could be explained was another indication that he should be classed as a nonscientist.

Finally, because he sought vindication from the lay public through the popular press, rather than through communication with scientists in the archival literature, he was criticized for failing to play the game properly—even though access to the scientific journals through regular channels was probably not open to him.

By all the informal standards scientists use to protect themselves from distraction, and their bodies of knowledge from disruption, Velikovsky could only be viewed as an outside threat to the scientific community, and he was treated accordingly. That he symbolized what scientists took to be a broad attack on the intellectual community as a whole surely accounts for much of the bitterness of their counterattack.

Further, once the scientific community was committed to opposing Velikovsky's assertions, it became a sign of disloyalty for a scientist to support Velikovsky's claims, or even to call for more open-mindedness on the part of colleagues. The forces of group loyalty took precedence over the usual idea of science as a disinterested quest for truth; and the particular aspects of the Velikovsky case noted above only strengthened scientists' sense of the legitimacy of their responses to him.

Conclusions

One corollary of my earlier statement about the importance to the scientific community of an organized universe of discourse is that a threat to its integrity is far more than simply a threat to a few scientists' reputations or positions. It is a threat to the very foundations, to the very meaning, of most scientists' professional careers.

Because an organized body of scientific knowledge is so important to the scientist's professional activities and identity, there is a natural tendency to view it as being more tightly integrated, more impervious to failure through internal inconsistency, than may actually be the case. But while faith in the integrity of scientific knowledge may occasionally be misplaced, this faith does serve as a useful first line of defense against all of the patently invalid claims and theories that circle continually outside the walls of science. Over the long run, the scientist's time is far better used if assertions of scientific truth coming from nonscientific sources are rejected out of hand—for instance, the claim that unusual weather patterns on Earth have been caused by the moon landings—than if each and every such claim is accepted seriously and patiently subjected to detailed testing.

Yet the history of science contains more than a few instances where scientists' faith in the validity and internal consistency of given bodies of knowledge turned out to be wrong. This is not to say that rejection by scientists automatically makes a theory correct, any more than that behavior by scientists that violates their own professed normative standards renders their beliefs incorrect. It is, instead, to point out that most of the time it requires a trained scientist to make a meaningful contribution to science, and that if the walls of the scientific community were to be breached so that *every* would-be contributor had to be taken seriously, the community would be literally destroyed.

Velikovsky and his supporters have run into these social facts about science, and it is clear that the collision has been painful. Yet given the circumstances, both those pertaining specifically to him and those characteristic of the broader situation, I would say that the controversy was inevitable.

Postscript. We sociologists of science have been saying for some time that the social character of science has important consequences for the ways and directions in which scientific knowledge develops. Knowledge does not exist independent of human and social concerns, even though our goal is to free empirical knowledge from such complications. It is inevitable, then, that human interests—the very meaning of careers, more importantly than particular individuals' positions and reputations—will be caught up whenever questions are raised over the validity of statements about empirical reality.

It is inevitable also that the consequences of human involvement in such questions can be construed in different ways. To some, Velikovsky has been a kind of "Mr. Smith Goes to Washington," who brings the virtues of unadorned honesty and a simple concern for the truth into the midst of a self-serving club of arrogant, powerful politicians. To others, he has been the loud, disputatious new kid from another neighborhood who jumps into the middle of an ongoing ball game and thoroughly disrupts it for the other players.

Truth, of course, is not really at stake. The truth about the history of the solar system *is* the truth, whether we have discovered it or are in error about it. As we come to understand more about the dynamics of the scientific community, I hope we may be able to arrive at scientific truth without spending quite so much energy and emotion on procedural side issues. On the other hand, though, we shall never separate scientific knowledge from scientists; and as long as scientists are human and make up a human community, we shall continue to be reminded, as by Velikovsky's challenge to the scientific community, that science is heir to most of the difficulties and weaknesses that beset all human groups.

Notes

1. Robert K. Merton, *The Sociology of Science: Theoretical and Empirical Investigations* (Chicago: University of Chicago Press, 1973).
2. Thomas S. Kuhn, *The Structure of Scientific Revolutions* (Chicago: University of Chicago Press, 1962).
3. Alfred de Grazia, ed., *The Velikovsky Affair* (New Hyde Park, N.Y.: University Books, 1966).

2 An Analysis of *Worlds in Collision*

CARL SAGAN

When the movement of the comets is considered and we reflect on the laws of gravity, it will be readily perceived that their approach to the Earth might there cause the most woeful events, bring back the universal deluge, or make it perish in a deluge of fire, shatter it into small dust, or at least turn it from its orbit, drive away its Moon, or, still worse, the Earth itself outside the orbit of Saturn, and inflict upon us a winter several centuries long, which neither men nor animals would be able to bear. The tails even of comets would not be unimportant phenomena, if the comets in taking their departure left them in whole or in part in our atmosphere.

—Lambert, *Lettres cosmologiques* (1767)

However dangerous might be the shock of a comet, it might be so slight, that it would only do damage at the part of the Earth where it actually struck; perhaps even we might cry quits if while one kingdom were devastated, the rest of the Earth were to enjoy the rarities which a body which came from so far might bring to it. Perhaps we should be very surprised to find that the debris of these masses that we despised were formed of gold and diamonds; but who would be the most astonished, we, or the comet-dwellers, who would be cast on our Earth? What strange beings each would find the other!

—Maupertuis, *Lettre sur la comete* (1752)

Introduction

Scientists, like other human beings, have their hopes and fears, their passions and despondencies—and their strong emotions may sometimes interrupt the course of clear thinking and sound practice. But science is also self-correcting: the most fundamental axioms and conclusions may be challenged; the prevailing hypotheses must survive confrontation with observation; appeals to authority are impermissible; the steps in a reasoned argument must be set out for all to see; experiments must be reproducible. The history of science is full of cases where previously accepted theories and hypotheses have been entirely overthrown, to be replaced by new ideas which more adequately explain the data. While there is an understandable psychological inertia, usually lasting about one generation, such revolutions in scientific thought are widely accepted as a necessary and desirable element of scientific progress. Indeed, the reasoned criticism of a prevailing belief is a service to the proponents of that belief; if they are incapable of defending it, they are well advised to abandon it. This self-questioning and error-correcting aspect of the scientific method is its most striking property, and sets it off from many other areas of human endeavor, such as politics and theology.

The idea of science as a method rather than as a body of knowledge is not widely appreciated outside of science; or indeed in some corridors inside of science. For this reason I and some other of my colleagues in the AAAS have advocated a regular set of discussions at the annual AAAS meeting of hypotheses which are on the borderlines of science and which have attracted substantial public interest. The idea is not to attempt definitively to settle such issues, but rather to illustrate the process of reasoned disputation, and perhaps to show how scientists approach a problem which does not lend itself to crisp experimentation, or is unorthodox in its interdisciplinary nature, or otherwise evokes strong emotions. Some scientists have resisted holding such meetings; for example, the 1969 AAAS symposium on Unidentified Flying Objects (UFO's) was predicted by some to threaten the very fabric of science. But the meeting was held, the proceedings published (Sagan and Page, 1972) and the fabric of science remains untorn. I even think that it may have gained some shear and tensile strength from the experience.

Vigorous criticism of new ideas is a commonplace in science. While the style of the critique may vary with the character of the critic, overly polite criticism benefits neither the proponents of new ideas nor the scientific enterprise. Any substantive objection is permissible and encouraged, the only exception being that *ad hominem* attacks on the personality or motives of the author are excluded. It does not matter what reason the proponent has for advancing his ideas or what prompts his opponents to criticize them: all that matters is whether the ideas are right or wrong, promising or retrogressive. (The situation is, evidently, the reverse of what passes for reasoned discourse in politics and many other areas of contemporary life.)

For example, here is a summary, of a type which is unusual but not extremely rare, of a paper submitted to the scientific journal *Icarus*, by a qualified referee: "It is the opinion of this reviewer that this paper is absolutely unacceptable for publication in *Icarus*. It is based on no sound scientific research, and at best it is incompetent speculation. The author has not stated his assumptions; the conclusions are unclear, ambiguous and without basis; credit is not given to related work; the figures and tables are unclearly labled; and the author is obviously unfamiliar with the most basic scientific literature. . . ." The referee then goes on to justify his remarks in detail. The paper was rejected for publication. Such rejections are commonly recognized as a boon to science as well as a favor to the author. Most scientists are accustomed to receiving (somewhat milder) referees' criticisms every time they submit a paper to a scientific journal. Almost always the criticisms are helpful. Often a paper that is revised to take these critiques into account is subsequently accepted for publication. As another example of forthright criticism in the planetary science literature, the interested reader might wish to consult "Comments on *The Jupiter Effect*" by Jean Meeus (1975) and the following commentary in *Icarus*. Vigorous criticism is constructive in science more than in some other areas of human endeavor, because in it there are adequate standards of validity which can be agreed upon by competent practitioners the world over. The objective of such criticism is not to suppress but rather to encourage the advance of new ideas: those which survive a firm skeptical scrutiny have a fighting chance of being right or at least useful.

Emotions in the scientific community have run very high on the issue of Immanuel Velikovsky's work, especially his first book, *Worlds in Collision*, published in 1950. I know that some scientists were irked because Velikovsky was compared to Einstein, Newton, Darwin, and Freud by New York literati and the jazz editor of *Harper's*, but this pique arises from the frailty of human nature rather than the judgment of the scientist. The two together often inhabit the same individual. Others were dismayed at the use of Indian, Chinese, Aztec, Assyrian, or Biblical texts to argue for extremely heterodox views in celestial mechanics. Also, I suspect, not many physicists or celestial mechanicians are comfortably fluent in such languages or are familiar with such texts.

My own strongly held view is that no matter how unorthodox the reasoning process or how unpalatable the conclusions, there is no excuse for any attempt to suppress new ideas, least of all by scientists committed to the free exchange of ideas. Therefore I was very pleased that the AAAS agreed to hold this discussion. In reading the critical literature on *Worlds in Collision*, I am surprised at how little of it there is and how rarely it approaches the central points of Velikovsky's thesis. In fact, I seem to find that neither the critics nor the proponents of Velikovsky have read him carefully; and I even seem to find some cases where Velikovsky has not read Velikovsky carefully. Perhaps this publication will help to clarify the issues.

The Uniformitarians and the Catastrophists

In this chapter I have tried to analyze critically the thesis of *Worlds in Collision.* I have attempted to approach the problem both on Velikovsky's terms and on mine—that is, to keep firmly in mind the ancient writings which are the focus of his argument, but at the same time to confront his conclusions with whatever facts and logic I have at my command.

Velikovsky's principal thesis is that major events in the history of both the Earth and the other planets in the solar system have been dominated by Catastrophism, rather than Uniformitarianism. These are fancy words used by geologists to summarize a major debate they had during the infancy of their science, a debate that apparently culminated between 1785 and 1830 in the work of James Hutton and Charles Lyell in favor of the Uniformitarians. Both the names and the practices of these two sects evoke familiar theological antecedents. A Uniformitarian holds that land forms on the Earth have been produced by processes which we can observe to be operating today, provided they operate over immense vistas of time. A Catastrophist holds that a small number of violent events, occupying much shorter periods of time, are adequate to effect the changes we see. Catastrophism began largely in the minds of those geologists who accepted a literal interpretation of the Book of *Genesis,* and in particular the account of the Noachic flood. It is clearly no use arguing against the Catastrophist viewpoint that we have never seen such a catastrophe in our lifetimes. The hypothesis requires only rare events. But if we can show that there is adequate time for processes which we can all observe operating today to produce the land form or event in question, then there is at least no necessity for the Catastrophist hypothesis. Obviously both uniformitarian and catastrophic processes can have been at work—and almost certainly both were—in the history of our planet.

Velikovsky holds that there have been in the relatively recent history of the Earth a set of celestial catastrophes, near collisions with comets, small planets, and large planets. There is nothing absurd in the possibility of cosmic collisions. Astronomers in the past have not hesitated to invoke collisions to explain natural phenomena. For example, Lyman Spitzer and Walter Baade (1951) proposed that extragalactic radio sources may be produced by the collisions of whole galaxies that contain hundreds of billions of stars. This thesis has now been abandoned, not because cosmic collisions are unthinkable, but because the frequency and properties of such collisions do not match what is now known about such radio sources. Likewise a still popular theory of the energy source of quasars is multiple stellar collisions at the centers of galaxies, where, in any case, catastrophic events must be common.

Collisions and catastrophism are part and parcel of modern astronomy, and have been for many centuries (see the epigraphs at the beginning of this chapter). For example, in the early history of the solar system, when there were probably many more objects about than there are now—including objects on very eccentric orbits—collisions may have been frequent. In a recent effort to understand the present configuration of the asteroid region of the solar system, Myron Lecar and Fred A. Franklin (1973) investigated hundreds of collisions occurring in a period of only a few thousand years in the early history of the asteroid belt. In another recent paper, "Cometary Collisions and Geological Periods," Harold Urey (1973) investigated a range of consequences, including the production of earthquakes and the heating of the oceans, which might attend the collision with the Earth of a comet of average mass of about 10^{18} grams. The Tunguska event of 1908, in which a Siberian forest was leveled, is often attributed to the collision with the Earth of a small comet. The cratered surfaces of Mercury, Mars, Phobos, Deimos, and the moon bear eloquent testimony to the fact that there have been abundant collisions during the history of the solar system. There is nothing unorthodox about the idea of cosmic catastrophes, and this is a view which has been common in solar-system physics at least back to the late nineteenth-century studies of the lunar surface by Grove Karl Gilbert, the first director of the U.S. Geological Survey.

What then is all the furor about? It is about the time scale and the adequacy of the purported evidence. In the 4.5-billion-year history of the solar system, many collisions must have occurred. But have there been major collisions in the last thirty-five hundred years, and can the study of ancient writings demonstrate such collisions? That is the nub of the issue.

The Method of Concordances in Myth and Legend

Velikovsky has called attention to a wide range of stories and legends held by diverse peoples who are separated by great distances, stories which show remarkable similarities and concordances. I am not expert in the cultures or languages of any of these peoples, but I find the concatenation of legends which Velikovsky has accumulated stunning. It is true that some experts in these cultures are less impressed. I can vividly remember discussing *Worlds in Collision* with a distinguished professor of Semitics at a leading university. He said something like "The Assyriology, Egyptology, Biblical scholarship and all of that Talmudic and midrashic *pilpul* is of course nonsense; but I was impressed by the astronomy." I had rather the opposite view. But let me not be swayed by the opinions of others. My own position is that even if twenty percent of the legendary concordances which Velikovsky produces are real, there is something important to be explained. Furthermore, there is an impressive array of cases in the history of archaeology—from Heinrich Schliemann at Troy to Yigael Yadin at Masada—where the descriptions in ancient writings have subsequently been validated as fact.

Now if a variety of widely separated cultures share what is palpably the same legend, how can this be understood? There seem to be four possibilities: common observation, diffusion, brain wiring, and coincidence. I consider these in turn.

Common Observation. The cultures in question all witnessed a common event and interpreted it in the same way. There may, of course, be more than one view of what this common event was.

Diffusion. The legend originated within one culture only, but during the frequent and distant migrations of mankind, gradually spread and slowly changed as it passed from culture to culture. A trivial example is the Santa Claus legend in America, which evolved from the European Saint Nicholas (Claus is short for Nicholas in German), the patron saint of children, and which ultimately is derived from pre-Christian tradition.

Brain Wiring. A hypothesis also sometimes known as racial memory or the collective unconscious. It holds that there are certain ideas, archetypes, legendary figures, and stories which are intrinsic to human beings at birth, perhaps in the same way that a newborn baboon knows to fear a snake and a bird raised in isolation from other birds knows how to build a nest. It is apparent that if a tale derived from observation or from diffusion resonates with the "brain wiring," it is more likely to be culturally retained.

Coincidence. Purely by chance two independently derived legends may have similar content. In practice, this hypothesis fades into the brain-wiring hypothesis.

If we are to assess critically such apparent concordances, there are some obvious precautions that must first be taken. Do the stories really say the same thing or have the same essential elements? If they are interpreted as due to common observations, do they date from the same period? Can we exclude the possibility of physical contact between representatives of the cultures in question in or before the epoch under discussion? Velikovsky is clearly opting for the common-observation hypothesis, but he seems to dismiss the diffusion hypothesis far too casually; for example (page 303),* he says, "How could unusual motifs of folklore reach isolated islands where the aborigines do not have any means of crossing the sea?" I am not sure which islands and which aborigines Velikovsky refers to here, but it is apparent that the inhabitants of an island had to have gotten there somehow. I do not think that Velikovsky believes in a separate creation in the Gilbert and Ellice Islands, say. For Polynesia and Melanesia there is now extensive evidence of abundant

* The page numbers refer to the canonical English-language edition (Velikovsky, 1950).

sea voyages of lengths of many thousands of kilometers within the last millennium, and probably much earlier (see, e.g., Dodd, 1972).

Or how, for example, would Velikovsky explain the fact that the Toltec name for "God" seems to have been "Teo," as in the great pyramid city of Teotihaucán (City of the Gods) near present-day Mexico City, where it is called San Juan Teotihaucán? There is no common celestial event which could conceivably explain this concordance. Toltec and Nahuatl are non-Indo-European languages, and it seems unlikely that the word for god would be wired into all human brains. Yet Teo is a clear cognate of the common Indoeuropean root for god, preserved, among other places, in the words "deity" and "theology." The preferred hypotheses in this case are coincidence or diffusion. There is some evidence for pre-Columbian contact between Old and New Worlds. But coincidence is also not to be taken lightly. If we compare two languages, each with tens of thousands of words, spoken by human beings with identical larynxes, tongues, and teeth, it should not be surprising if a few words are coincidentally identical. Likewise, we should not be surprised if a few elements of a few legends are coincidentally identical. But I do not believe that all of the concordances which Velikovsky produces can be explained away in this manner.

Let us take an example of Velikovsky's approach to this question. He points to certain concordant stories, directly or vaguely connected with celestial events, which refer to a witch, a mouse, a scorpion, or a dragon (pages 77, 264, 305, 306, 310). His explanation: divers comets, upon close approach to the Earth, were tidally or electrically distorted and appeared as a witch, a mouse, a scorpion, or a dragon, clearly interpretable as the same animal, to culturally isolated peoples of very different backgrounds. No attempt is made to show that such a clear form—for example, a woman riding a broomstick and topped by a pointed hat—could have been produced in this way, even if we grant the hypothesis of a close approach to the Earth by a comet. Our experience with Rorschach and other psychological projective tests gives clear proof that different people will see the same nonrepresentational image in different ways. Velikovsky even goes so far as to believe that a close approach to the Earth by the planet Mars so distorted the shape of Mars that it took on the appearance (page 264) of a lion, a jackal, a dog, a pig, or a fish; and goes on to say that in his opinion this explains the worship of animals by the Egyptians. This is not very impressive reasoning. We might just as well assume that the whole menagerie was capable of independent flight in the second millennium B.C. and be done with it. A much more likely hypothesis is diffusion. Indeed, I have in a different context spent a fair amount of time studying the dragon legends on the planet Earth, and I am impressed at how different these mythical beasts, all called dragons by Western writers, really are.

As another example, consider the argument of Chapter 8, Part 2, of *Worlds in Collision*. Velikovsky claims a world-wide tendency in ancient cultures to believe at various times that the year has 360 days, that the month has 30 days, and that—of course, inconsistent with the above two beliefs—the year has ten months. Velikovsky argues that ancient astronomers could hardly have been so poor at their trade as to slip five days each year or a half-day each lunation. Fairly soon the night would be brilliant with moonlight at astrologically official new moon, snowstorms would be falling in July, and the astrologers would be hung by their ears. Having had some experience with modern astronomers, I am not as confident as Velikovsky in the computational precision of ancient astronomers. Velikovsky proposes that these aberrant calendrical conventions are due to real changes in the length of the day, month, and/or year, and that they are evidence of close approaches to the Earth-moon system by comets, planets, and other celestial visitors.

There is an alternative explanation, which derives from the fact that there are not a whole number of lunations in a solar year, nor a whole number of days in a lunation. These incommensurabilities would be galling to a culture which had recently invented arithmetic but which had not yet gotten as far as large numbers or fractions. As an inconvenience, these incommensurabilities are felt even today by religious Muslims and

Jews who discover that Ramadan and Passover, respectively, occur from year to year on rather different days of the solar calendar. There is a clear whole-number chauvinism in human affairs, most easily discerned in discussing arithmetic with four-year-olds; and this seems to be a much more plausible explanation of these calendrical irregularities, if they existed. Three hundred sixty days a year provide an obvious (temporary) convenience for a civilization with base-sixty arithmetic, as in the Sumerian, Akkadian, Assyrian, and Babylonian cultures. Likewise, thirty days per month or ten months per year might be attractive to enthusiasts of base-ten arithmetic. I wonder if we do not see here an echo of the collision between chauvinists of base-sixty arithmetic and chauvinists of base-ten arithmetic, rather than a collision of Mars with the Earth. It is true that the tribe of ancient astrologers may have been dramatically depleted as the various calendars rapidly slipped out of phase, but that was an occupational hazard in any case, and at least it removed the mental agony of dealing with fractions. In fact, sloppy quantitative thinking appears to be the hallmark of this whole subject.

An expert on early time-reckoning (Leach, 1954) points out that in ancient cultures the first eight or ten months of the year are named, but the last few months, because of their economic unimportance in an agricultural society, are not. Our month December, named after the Latin *decem*, means the tenth, not the twelfth month. (September = 7, October = 8, November = 9, as well.) Because of the large numbers involved, prescientific peoples characteristically did not count days of the year, although they were assiduous in counting months. A leading historian of ancient science and mathematics, Otto Neugebauer (1957) remarks that both in Mesopotamia and in Egypt, two separate and mutually exclusive calendars were maintained: a civil calendar whose hallmark was computational convenience, and a frequently updated agricultural calendar—messier to deal with, but much closer to the seasonal and astronomical realities. Many ancient cultures solved the two-calendar problem by simply adding a five-day holiday at the end of the year. I hardly think that the existence of 360-day years in the calendrical conventions of prescientific peoples is compelling evidence that then there really were 360 rather than 365 rotations in one revolution of the Earth about the Sun.

This question can, in principle, be resolved by examining coral growth rings, which are now known to show with some accuracy the number of days per month and the number of days per year, the former only for intertidal corals. There appear to be no signs of major excursions in recent times from the present number of days in a lunation or a year; and the gradual shortening (not lengthening) of the day and the month with respect to the year as we go back in time is found to be consistent with tidal theory and the conservation of energy and angular momentum within the earth-moon system, without appeal to cometary or other exogenous intervention.

Another problem with Velikovsky's method is the suspicion that vaguely similar stories may refer to quite different periods. This question of the synchronism of legends is almost entirely ignored in *Worlds in Collision,* although it is treated in some of Velikovsky's later works. For example (page 31), Velikovsky notes that the idea of four ancient ages terminated by catastrophe is common to Indian as well as to Western sacred writing. However, in the *Bhagavad-Gita* and in the *Vedas,* widely divergent numbers of such ages, including an infinity of them, are given; but, more interestingly, the duration of the ages between major catastrophes is specified (see, e.g., Campbell, 1974) as some 4.3 billion years, entrancingly close to the actual age of the solar system. This does not match very well with Velikovsky's chronology, which requires hundreds or thousands of years. Here Velikovsky's hypothesis, and the data which purport to support it, differ by a factor of about a million. Or (page 91) vaguely similar discussions of volcanism and lava flows in Greek, Mexican, and Biblical traditions are quoted. There is no attempt made to show that they refer to even approximately comparable times and, since lava has flowed in historical times in all three areas, no common exogenous event is necessary to interpret such stories.

Despite copious references, there also seem to me to be a large number of critical and undemonstrated assumptions in Velikovsky's argument. Let me mention just a few of them. There is the very interesting idea that any mythological references, by any people, to any god which also corresponds to a celestial body represent in fact a direct observation of that celestial body. It is a daring and interesting hypothesis, although I am not sure what one is to do with Jupiter appearing as a swan to Leda, and as a shower of gold to Danaë. On page 247 the hypothesis that gods and planets are identical is used to date the time of Homer. In any case, when Hesiod and Homer refer to Athena being born full-grown from the head of Zeus, Velikovsky takes Hesiod and Homer at their word and assumes that the celestial body Athena was ejected by the planet Jupiter. But what *is* the celestial body Athena? Repeatedly it is identified with the planet Venus (Part 1, Chapter 9, and many other places in the text). One would scarcely guess from reading *Worlds in Collision* that the Greeks characteristically identified Aphrodite with Venus, and Athena with no celestial body whatever. What is more, Athena and Aphrodite were "contemporaneous" goddesses, both being born at the time Zeus was king of the gods. On page 251 Velikovsky notes that Lucian "is unaware that Athena is the goddess of the planet Venus." Poor Lucian seems to be under the misconception that Aphrodite is the goddess of the planet Venus. But in the footnote on page 361 there seems to be a slip, and here Velikovsky uses for the first and only time the form "Venus (Aphrodite)." On page 247 we hear of Aphrodite, the goddess of the moon. Who then was Artemis, the sister of Apollo the sun, or, earlier, Selene? There may be good justification, for all I know, in identifying Athena with Venus, but it is far from the prevailing wisdom either now or two thousand years ago, and it is central to Velikovsky's argument. It does not increase our confidence in the presentation of less familiar myths when the celestial identification of Athena is glossed over so lightly.

Other critical statements which are given extremely inadequate justification, and which are central to one or more of

Velikovsky's major themes, are as follows: the statement (page 283) that "Meteorites, when entering the earth's atmosphere, make a frightful din," when they are generally observed to be silent; the statement (page 114) that "a thunderbolt, when striking a magnet, reverses the poles of the magnet;" the translation (page 51) of "barad" as meteorites; and the contention (page 85) "as is known, Pallas was another name for Typhon." On page 179 is enunciated a principle that when two gods are hypenated in a joint name, it indicates an attribute of a celestial body—as, for example, Ashteroth-Karnaim, a horned Venus, which Velikovsky interprets as a crescent Venus and as evidence that Venus was once close enough to the Earth to have its phases discernible to the naked eye. But what does this principle imply, for example, for the god Ammon-Ra? Did the Egyptians see the sun (Ra) as a ram (Ammon)?

There is a contention (page 63) that instead of the tenth plague of the *Exodus* killing the "first born" of Egypt, what is intended is the killing of the "chosen." This is a rather serious matter, and at least raises the suspicion that where the Bible is inconsistent with Velikovsky's hypothesis. Velikovsky retranslates the Bible. The foregoing queries may all have simple answers, but the answers are not to be found easily in *Worlds in Collision*.

I do not mean to suggest that all of Velikovsky's legendary concordances and ancient scholarship are similarly flawed, but much of it seems to be; and the remainder may well have alternative, for example diffusionist, origins.

With the situation in legend and myth as fuzzy as this, any corroboratory evidence from other sources would be welcomed by those who support Velikovsky's argument. I am struck by the absence of any confirming evidence in art. There is a wide range of paintings, bas-reliefs, cylinder seals, and other *objects d'art* produced by humankind and going back at least to tens of thousands of years B.C. They represent all of the subjects—especially mythological subjects—important to the cultures which created them. Astronomical events are not uncommon in such works of art. Recently (Brandt et al., 1974), impressive evidence has been uncovered in cave paintings in the American Southwest of contemporary observations of the Crab Supernova event of the year 1054, which was also recorded in Chinese, Japanese, and Korean annals. Appeals have been made to archaeologists for information on cave-painting representations of the earlier Gum Supernova (Brandt et. al., 1971). But supernova events are not nearly so impressive as the close approach of another planet with attendant interplanetary tendrils and lightning discharges connecting it to the Earth. There are many unflooded caves at high altitudes, distant from the sea. If the Velikovskian catastrophes occurred, why are there no contemporary graphic records of them?

I therefore cannot find the legendary base of Velikovsky's hypothesis at all compelling. If, nevertheless, his hypothesis of planetary collisions and global catastrophism were strongly supported by physical evidence, we might be tempted to give it some credence. If the physical evidence is, however, not very strong, the mythological evidence will surely not stand by itself.

Velikovsky's Principal Hypothesis

Let me now give a short summary of my understanding of the basic features of Velikovsky's principal hypothesis. I will relate it to the events described in the Book of *Exodus,* although the stories of many other cultures are said to be consistent with the events described in *Exodus*.

The planet Jupiter disgorged a large comet, which made a grazing collision with the Earth around 1500 B.C. The various plagues and Pharaonic tribulations of the Book of *Exodus* all derive directly or indirectly from this cometary encounter: material which made the river Nile turn to blood drops from the comet; the vermin described in *Exodus* are produced by the comet; flies and perhaps scarabs drop out of the comet, while indigenous terrestrial frogs are induced by the heat of the comet to multiply; and earthquakes produced by the comet level Egyptian but not Hebrew dwellings. (The only thing that does not seem to drop from the comet is cholesterol to harden Pharoah's heart.)

All this evidently falls from the coma of the comet, because at the moment that Moses strikes his staff upon the rock, the Red Sea parts—due either to the gravitational tidal field of the comet, or to some unspecified electrical or magnetic interaction between the comet and the Red Sea. Then, when the Hebrews have successfully crossed, the comet has evidently passed sufficiently further on for the parted waters to flow back and drown the host of Pharoah. The Children of Israel during their subsequent forty years of wandering in the Wilderness of Sin are nourished by manna from heaven, which turns out to be hydrocarbons (or carbohydrates) from the tail of the comet. Another reading of *Worlds in Collision* makes it appear that the plagues and the Red Sea events represent two different passages of the comet, separated by a month or two. Then after the death of Moses and the passing of the mantle of leadership to Joshua, the same comet comes screeching back for another grazing collision with the Earth. At the moment that Joshua says, "Sun, stand thou still upon Gibeon; and thou, Moon, in the valley of Agalon," the Earth—perhaps because of tidal interaction, again, or perhaps because of an unspecified magnetic induction in the crust of the Earth—obligingly ceases its rotation, to permit Joshua victory in battle. The comet then makes a near collision with Mars, so violent as to eject it out of *its* orbit, so that it makes two near collisions with the Earth which destroy the army of Sennacherib, the Assyrian king, as he was making life miserable for some subsequent generation of Israelites. The net result was to eject Mars into its present orbit and the comet into a circular orbit around the sun, where it became the planet Venus. The Earth meantime had somehow begun rotating again at almost exactly the same rate as before these encounters. No subsequent aberrant planetary behavior has occurred since about the sixth century B.C., although it might have been common in the second millennium.

That this is a remarkable story, no one—proponents and opponents alike—will disagree. Whether it is a likely story is, fortunately, amenable to scientific inquiry. Velikovsky's hypothesis makes certain predictions: that comets are ejected from planets;

that comets are likely to make near or grazing collisions with planets; that vermin live in comets and in the atmospheres of Jupiter and Venus; that carbohydrates can be found in the same places; that enough carbohydrates fell in the Sinai peninsula for nourishment during forty years of wandering in the desert; that eccentric cometary or planetary orbits can be circularized in a period of hundreds of years; that volcanic and tectonic events on the Earth and impact events on the moon were contemporaneous with these catastrophes; and so on. We will discuss each of these ideas, as well as some others—for example, that the surface of Venus is hot, which is clearly less central to his hypothesis, but which has been widely advertised as powerful *post hoc* support of it. We will also examine an occasional additional "prediction" of Velikovsky—for example, that the Martian polar caps are carbon or carbohydrates. My conclusion will be that where Velikovsky is original he is very likely wrong; and that where he is right the idea has been pre-empted by earlier workers. There are also a large number of cases (see the epigraphs of this article) where he is neither right nor original. The question of originality is important because of circumstances—for example, the high surface temperature of Venus—which are said to have been predicted by Velikovsky at a time when everyone else was imagining an Earth-like Venus. As we shall see, this is not quite the case.

In the following discussion we will try to use simple quantitative reasoning as much as possible. Quantitative arguments are obviously a finer mesh with which to sift hypotheses than qualitative arguments. For example, if I say that a large tidal wave engulfed the Earth, there is a wide range of catastrophes—from the flooding of littoral regions to global inundation—which might be pointed to as support for my contention. But if I specify a tide one hundred miles high, I can only be talking about the latter, and, moreover, there might be some critical evidence to counterindicate or support a tide of such dimensions. However, so as to make the quantitative arguments tractable to the reader who is not very familiar with elementary physics, I have tried, particularly in the appendixes, to state all the essential steps in the quantitative development, using the simplest arguments which preserve the essential physics. Perhaps I need not mention that such quantitative testing of hypotheses is entirely routine in the physical and biological sciences today. By rejecting the hypotheses which do not meet these standards of analysis, we are able to move swiftly to hypotheses in better concordance with the facts.

There is one further point about scientific method which must be made. Not all scientific statements have equal weight. Newtonian dynamics and the laws of conservation of energy and angular momentum are on extremely firm footing. Literally millions of separate experiments have been performed on their validity—not just on the Earth, but, using the observational techniques of modern astrophysics, elsewhere in the solar system, in multiple star systems, and even in other galaxies. On the other hand, questions on the nature of planetary surfaces, atmospheres, and interiors are on much weaker footing, as the substantial debates on these matters by planetary scientists in recent years clearly indicate. A good example of this distinction is given by the recent appearance of Comet Kohoutek. This comet had first been observed at a great distance from the sun. On the basis of the early observations, two predictions were made. The first concerned the orbit of Comet Kohoutek—where it would be found at future times, when it would be observable from the Earth before sunrise, when after sunset—predictions based on Newtonian dynamics. These predictions were correct to within a gnat's eyelash. The second prediction concerned the brightness of the comet. This was based on the guessed rate of vaporization of cometary ices to make a large cometary tail which brightly reflects sunlight. This prediction was painfully in error, and the comet, far from rivaling Venus in brightness, could not be seen at all by most naked-eye observers. The same distinction, between well-founded scientific arguments and arguments based on a physics or chemistry that we do not fully understand, must be borne in mind in any analysis of *Worlds in Collision*. Arguments based on Newtonian dynamics or the great conservation laws of physics must be given very substantial weight. Arguments based on planetary-surface properties, for example, must have correspondingly lesser weights. We will find that Velikovsky's arguments run into extremely grave difficulties on both these scores, but the one set of difficulties is far more damaging than the other.

PROBLEM I. THE EJECTION OF VENUS BY JUPITER

Velikovsky's hypothesis begins with an event which has never been observed by astronomers and which is inconsistent with much that we know about planetary and cometary physics, namely, the ejection of an object of planetary dimensions from Jupiter. From the fact that the aphelia of the orbits of short-period comets have a statistical tendency to lie near Jupiter, Pierre Simon, Marquis de Laplace and other early astronomers hypothesized that Jupiter was the source of such comets. This is an unnecessary hypothesis because we now know that long-period comets may be transferred to short-period trajectories by the perturbations of the planet Jupiter, and this view has not been advocated for a century or two, except by the Soviet astronomer V. S. Vsekhsviatsky, who seems to believe that the moons of Jupiter eject comets out of giant volcanoes.

To escape from Jupiter, such a comet must have a kinetic energy of $\frac{1}{2} mv_e^2$, where m is the cometary mass and v_e is the escape velocity from Jupiter, which is about 70 km/sec. Whatever the ejection event—volcanoes or collisions—some significant fraction, at least 10 percent, of this kinetic energy will go into heating the comet. The minimum kinetic energy per unit mass ejected is then $\frac{1}{2} v_e^2 = 2.5 \times 10^{13}$ ergs per gram, and the quantity which goes into heating is more than 2.5×10^{12} ergs/gm. The latent heat of fusion of rock is about 4×10^9 ergs/gm. This is the heat which must be applied to convert hot solid rock near the melting point to a fluid lava. About 10^{11} ergs/gm must be applied to raise rocks at low temperatures to their melting point. Thus, any event which would have ejected a comet or a planet from Jupiter would have brought it to a temperature of at least several thousands of degrees and, whether composed of rocks, ices, or organic compounds, would have completely melted it. It is even more likely that it would have been entirely reduced to a rain of self-gravitating small dust particles and atoms, which does not describe the planet Venus particularly well. The likelihood of a planet, much less an icy comet, surviving ejection seems small. (Incidentally, this would appear to be a good Velikovskian argument for the high temperature of the surface of Venus; but, as described below, this is not the argument.)

Another problem is that the escape velocity from the sun's gravity at the distance of Jupiter is about 20 km/sec. The ejection mechanism from Jupiter, of course, does not know this. Thus, if ejection occurs at velocities less than about 70 km/sec, the comet will fall back to Jupiter; if greater than about $[(20)^2 + (70)^2]^{\frac{1}{2}} = 73$ km/sec, it will escape from the solar system. There is only a narrow and therefore unlikely range of velocities which is consistent with Velikovsky's hypothesis, even apart from vaporization of the comet.

A further problem is that the mass of Venus is very large—more than 5×10^{27} gm, or possibly larger originally—on Velikovsky's hypothesis, before it passed close to the sun. The total kinetic energy required to propel Venus to Jovian escape velocity is then easily calculated to be on the order of 10^{41} ergs, which is equivalent to all the energy radiated by the sun to space in an entire year, and one hundred million times more powerful than the largest solar flare ever observed. We are asked to believe, without any further evidence or discussion, an ejection event vastly more powerful than anything on the sun, which is a far more energetic object than Jupiter.

Any process which makes large objects makes more small objects. This is especially true in a situation which is dominated by collisions, as in Velikovsky's hypothesis. Here the comminution physics is well known, and a particle one-tenth as large as our biggest particle should be a hundred or a thousand times more abundant. Indeed, Velikovsky has stones falling from the skies in the wake of his hypothesized planetary encounters, and imagines Venus and Mars trailing swarms of boulders; the Mars swarm, he says, led to the destruction of the armies of Sennacherib. But if this is true, if we had near collisions with objects of planetary mass only thousands of years ago, we should have been bombarded by objects of lunar mass hundreds of years ago, and bombardment by objects which can make craters a mile or so across should be happening every second Tuesday. Yet there is no sign, either on the Earth or the moon, of frequent recent collisions with such lower-mass objects. Instead, the few objects which, as a steady-state population, are moving in orbits which might collide with the moon are just adequate, over geological time, to explain the number of craters observed on the lunar maria. The absence of *a great many* small objects with orbits crossing the orbit of the Earth is another fundamental objection to Velikovsky's basic thesis.

PROBLEM II. REPEATED COLLISIONS AMONG THE EARTH, VENUS, AND MARS

"That a comet may strike our planet is not very probable, but the idea is not absurd" (page 40). This is precisely correct: it only remains to calculate the probabilities, which Velikovsky has unfortunately left undone.

Fortunately, the relevant physics is extremely simple and can be performed to order of magnitude even without any consideration of gravitation. Objects on highly eccentric orbits, traveling from the vicinity of Jupiter to the vicinity of the Earth, are traveling at such high speeds that their mutual gravitational attraction to the object with which they are about to have a grazing collision plays a negligible role in determining the trajectory. The calculation is performed in Appendix 1, where we see that a single "comet" with aphelion (far point from the sun) near the orbit of Jupiter and perihelion (near point to the sun) inside the orbit of Venus should take at least thirty million years before it impacts the Earth. We also find in Appendix 1 that, if the object is a member of the currently observed family of objects on such trajectories, the lifetime against collision exceeds the age of the solar system. But let us take the number thirty million years to give the maximum quantitative bias in favor of Velikovsky. Therefore, the odds against a collision with the Earth in any given year is 3×10^7 to one; the odds against it in any given millennium are thirty thousand to one. But Velikovsky has (see, e.g., page 388) not one but *five* or *six* near collisions among Venus, Mars, and the Earth—all of which seem to be statistically independent events; that is, by his own account, there does not seem to be a regular set of grazing collisions determined by the relative orbital periods of the three planets. (If there were, we would have to ask the probability that so remarkable a play in the game of planetary billiards could arise within Velikovsky's time constraints.) If the probabilities are independent, then the joint probability of five such encounters in the same millennium is on the short side of $(3 \times 10^7/10^3)^{-5} = (3 \times 10^4)^{-5} = 4.1 \times 10^{-23}$, or odds of almost a hundred billion trillion to one. For six encounters in the same millennium the odds rise to $(3 \times 10^7/10^3)^{-6} = (3 \times 10^4)^{-6} = 7.3 \times 10^{-28}$, or about a trillion quadrillion to one. Actually, these are lower limits—both for the reason given above and because close encounters with Jupiter are likely to eject the impacting object from the solar system altogether, rather as Jupiter ejected the Pioneer 10 spacecraft from the solar system. Odds like these are a proper calibration of the validity of Velikovsky's hypothesis, even were there no other difficulties with it. Hypotheses with such small odds in their favor are usually said to be untenable. With the other problems mentioned both above and below, the probability that the full thesis of *Worlds in Collision* is correct becomes negligible.

PROBLEM III. THE EARTH'S ROTATION

Much of the indignation directed toward *Worlds in Collision* seems to have arisen from Velikovsky's interpretation of the story of Joshua and related legends as implying that the Earth's rotation was once braked to a halt. The image that the most outraged protesters seem to have had in mind is that shown in the movie version of H. G. Wells' story, "The Man Who Could Work Miracles": the Earth is miraculously stopped from rotating but, through an oversight, no provision is made for all objects not nailed down, which then continue moving at their usual rate and therefore fly off the Earth at a speed of a thousand miles per hour. But it is easy to see (Appendix 2) that a gradual deceleration of the Earth's rotation at 10^{-2}g or so could occur in a period of much less than a day. Then no one would fly off and even stalactites and other delicate geomorphological forms could have survived. Likewise, we see in Appendix 2 that the energy required to brake the Earth is not enough to melt it, although it would result in a noticeable increase in temperature: the oceans would have been raised to the boiling point of water, an event which seems to have been overlooked by Velikovsky's ancient sources.

These are, however, not the most serious objections to Velikovsky's exegesis of Joshua. Perhaps the most serious objection is rather at the other end. How does the Earth get started up again, rotating at approximately the same rate of spin? The Earth cannot do it by itself, because of the law of the conservation of angular momentum. Velikovsky does not even seem to be aware that this is a problem.

Nor is there any hint that braking the Earth to a "halt" by cometary collision is any less likely than any other resulting spin. In fact, the chance of precisely canceling the Earth's rotational angular momentum in a cometary encounter is tiny; and the probability that subsequent encounters, were they to occur, would start the Earth spinning again even approximately once every twenty-four hours is tiny squared.

Velikovsky is vague about the mechanism which is supposed to have braked the Earth's rotation. Perhaps it is tidal gravitational; perhaps it is magnetic. Both of these fields produce forces which decline very rapidly with distance. While gravity declines as the inverse square of the distance, tides decline as the inverse cube, and the tidal couple as the inverse sixth power. The magnetic dipole field declines as the inverse cube, and any equivalent magnetic tides fall off even more steeply than gravitational tides. Therefore, the braking effect is almost entirely at the distance of closest approach. The characteristic time of this closest approach is clearly about $2R/v$, where R is the radius of the Earth and v the relative velocity of the comet and the Earth. With v about 25 km/sec, the characteristic time works out to be under ten minutes. This is the full time available for the total effect of the comet on the rotation of the Earth. The corresponding acceleration is less than 0.1 g, so armies still do not fly off into space. But the characteristic time for acoustic propagation within the Earth—the minimum time for an exterior influence to make itself felt on the Earth as a whole—is 85 minutes. Thus, no cometary influence, even in grazing collision, could make the sun stand still upon Gibeon.

Velikovsky's account of the history of the Earth's rotation is difficult to follow. On page 236 we have an account of the motion of the sun in the sky which by accident conforms to the appearance and apparent motion of the sun as seen from the surface of Mercury, but not from the surface of the Earth; and on page 385 we seem to have an aperture to a wholesale retreat by Velikovsky—for here he suggests that what happened was not any change in the angular velocity of rotation of the Earth, but rather a motion in the course of a few hours of the angular momentum vector of the Earth from pointing approximately at right angles to the ecliptic plane, as it does today, to pointing in the direction of the sun, like the planet Uranus. Quite apart from extremely grave problems in the physics of this suggestion, it is inconsistent with Velikovsky's own argument, because earlier Velikovsky has laid great weight on the fact that Eurasian and Near-Eastern cultures reported prolonged day while North American cultures reported prolonged night. In this variant there would be no explanation of the reports from Mexico. I think I see in this instance Velikovsky hedging on or forgetting his own strongest arguments from ancient writings.

On page 386 we have a qualitative argument, not reproduced, claiming that the Earth could have been braked to a halt by a strong magnetic field. The field strength required is not mentioned but clearly (cf. similar calculations in Appendix 4) would have to be enormous. There is no sign in rock magnetization of terrestrial rocks ever having been subjected to such strong field strengths and, what is equally important, we have quite firm evidence from both Soviet and American spacecraft that the magnetic-field strength of Venus is negligibly small—far less than the Earth's own surface field of 0.5 gauss, which would itself have been inadequate for Velikovsky's purpose.

PROBLEM IV. TERRESTRIAL GEOLOGY AND LUNAR CRATERS

Reasonably enough, Velikovsky believes that a near collision of another planet with the Earth might have had dramatic consequences—by gravitational tidal, electrical, or magnetic influences (Velikovsky is not very clear on this). He believes (pages 96 and 97) "that in the days of the Exodus, when the world was shaken and rocked . . . *all* volcanoes vomited lava and *all* continents quaked" (my emphasis).

There seems little doubt that earthquakes would have accompanied such a near collision. Apollo lunar seismometers have found that moonquakes are most common during lunar perigee, when the Earth is closest to the moon; and there are at least some hints of earthquakes at the same time. But the claim that there were extensive lava flows and volcanism involving "all volcanoes" is quite another story. Volcanic lavas are easily dated and what Velikovsky should produce is a histogram of the number of lava flows on the Earth as a function of time. Such a histogram, I believe, will show that not all volcanoes were active between 1500 and 600 B.C., and that there is nothing particularly remarkable about the volcanism of that epoch.

Velikovsky believes (page 115) that reversals of the geomagnetic field are produced by cometary close approaches. Yet the record from rock magnetization is clear—such reversals occur about every million years, though not in the last few thousand; and they recur more or less like clockwork. Is there a clock in Jupiter which aims comets at the Earth every million years? The conventional view is that the Earth experiences a polarity reversal of the self-sustaining dynamo which produces the Earth's magnetic field; it seems a much more likely explanation.

Velikovsky's contention that mountain-building occurred a few thousand years ago is belied by all the geological evidence which puts those times at tens of millions of years ago and more. The idea that mammoths were deep-frozen by a rapid movement of the Earth's geographical pole a few thousands of years ago can be tested, for example, by C^{14} or amino-acid racemization dating. I should be very surprised if a very recent age results from such tests.

Velikovsky believes that the moon, not immune to the catastrophes which befell the Earth, had similar tectonic events occur on its surface a few thousand years ago, and that many of its craters were formed then (see Part II, Chapter 9). There are some problems with this idea as well. Samples returned from the moon in the Apollo missions show no rocks melted more recently than a few hundred million years ago.

Furthermore, if lunar craters were to have formed abundantly twenty-seven hundred years ago, there must have been a similar production at the same time of terrestrial craters larger than a kilometer across. Erosion on the Earth's surface is inadequate to remove any crater of this size in twenty-seven hundred years. Not only are there not large numbers of terrestrial craters of this size and age, there is not a single one. On these questions, Velikovsky seems to have ignored critical evidence. When the evidence is examined, it strongly counterindicates his hypothesis.

Velikovsky believes that the close passage of Venus or Mars to the Earth would have produced tides at least miles high (page 70 and 71); in fact, if these planets were ever tens of thousands of kilometers away, as he seems to think, the tides, both of water and of the solid body of our planet, would be hundreds of miles high. This is easily calculated from the height of the present water and body lunar tide, since the tide height is proportional to the mass of the tide-producing object and inversely proportional to the cube of the distance. To the best of my knowledge, there is no geological evidence for a global inundation of all parts of the world either in the eighth or in the fifteenth centuries B.C. If such floods occurred, even if they were brief, they should have left some clear trace in the geological record. And what of the archeological and paleontological evidence? Where are the extensive faunal extinctions of the correct date due to such floods? And where is the evidence of extensive melting in these centuries, near where the tidal distortion is greatest?

PROBLEM V. CHEMISTRY AND BIOLOGY OF THE TERRESTRIAL PLANETS

Velikovsky's thesis has some peculiar biological and chemical consequences, which are compounded by some straightforward confusions on simple matters. He seems not to know (page 16) that oxygen is produced by green-plant photosynthesis on the Earth. He makes no note of the fact that Jupiter is composed primarily of hydrogen and helium, while the atmosphere of Venus, which he supposes to have arisen inside of Jupiter, is composed mainly of carbon dioxide. Velikovsky holds that the manna which fell from the skies in the Sinai peninsula was of cometary origin and therefore that there are carbohydrates on both Jupiter and Venus. On the other hand, he quotes copious sources for fire and naphtha falling from the skies which he interprets as celestial petroleum ignited in the Earth's oxidizing atmosphere (pages 53 through 58). Because Velikovsky believes in the reality and identity of both sets of events, his book displays a sustained confusion of carbohydrates and hydrocarbons; and at some points it appears more likely that the Israelites were eating fusel oil rather than divine nutriment during their forty years wandering in the desert.

Reading the text is made still more difficult by the apparent conclusion (page 366) of Martian polar caps made of manna, which are described ambiguously as "probably in the nature of carbon." Carbohydrates have a strong 3.5 micron absorption feature, due to the stretching vibration of the carbon-hydrogen bond. No trace of this feature was observed in infrared spectra of the Martian polar caps taken by the Mariner 6 and 7 spacecraft in 1969. On the other hand, Mariners 6, 7, and 9 have acquired abundant evidence for frozen water and frozen carbon dioxide as the constitutents of the polar caps.

Velikovsky's insistence on a celestial origin of petroleum is difficult to understand. Some of the accounts, for example, in Herodotus, provide perfectly natural descriptions of the combustion of petroleum upon seepage to the surface in Mesopotamia and Iran. As Velikovsky himself points out (pages 55–56), the rain-of-fire and naphtha stories derive from precisely those parts of the Earth that have natural petroleum deposits. There is, therefore, a straightforward terrestrial explanation of the stories in question. The amount of downward seepage of petroleum in twenty-seven hundred years would not be very great. The difficulty in extracting petroleum from the Earth, which is the cause of certain practical problems today, would be greatly ameliorated if Velikovsky's hypothesis were true. It is also very difficult to understand on his hypothesis how it is, if oil fell from the skies in 1500 B.C., that petroleum deposits are intimately mixed with chemical and biological fossils of tens to hundreds of millions of years ago. But this circumstance is readily explicable if, as most geologists have concluded, petroleum arises from decaying vegetation of the Carboniferous and other early geological epochs, and not from comets.

Even stranger are Velikovsky's views on extraterrestrial life. He believes that much of the "vermin," and particularly the flies referred to in *Exodus*, really fell from his comet—although he hedges on the extraterrestrial origin of frogs, while approvingly quoting from the Iranian text, the *Bundahish* (page 183), which seems to admit a rain of cosmic frogs. Let us consider flies only. Shall we expect houseflies or *Drosophila melanogaster* in forthcoming explorations of the clouds of Venus and Jupiter? Will Velikovsky's hypothesis fall if no flies are found?

The idea that of all the organisms on the Earth, flies alone are of extraterrestrial origin is curiously reminiscent of Martin Luther's exasperated conclusion that, while the rest of life was created by God, the fly must have been created by the Devil because there is no conceivable practical use for it. But flies are perfectly respectable insects, closely related in anatomy, physiology, and biochemistry to the other *insecta*. The possibility that four and one-half billion years of independent evolution on Jupiter—even if it were a physically identical place to the Earth—would produce a creature indistinguishable from other terrestrial organisms is to misread the evolutionary process. Flies have the same enzymes, the same nucleic acids, and even the same genetic code (which translates nucleic acid information into protein information) as do all the other organisms on the Earth. There are too many intimate associations and identities between flies and other terrestrial organisms for them to have separate origins, as any serious investigation of flies clearly shows.

In *Exodus* 9, it is said that the cattle of Egypt all died but the cattle of the Children of Israel "died not one." In the same chapter we find a plague which affects flax and barley but not wheat or rye. This fine-tuned host-parasite specificity is very strange for cometary vermin with no prior biological contact with the Earth, but is readily explicable in terms of home-grown terrestrial vermin.

Then there is the curious fact that flies metabolize molecular oxygen. There is no oxygen on Jupiter, nor can there be, because oxygen is thermodynamically unstable in an excess of hydrogen. Are we to imagine that the entire terminal electron-transfer apparatus required to deal with molecular oxygen was adventitiously evolved on Jupiter by Jovian organisms hoping someday to be transported to Earth? This would be yet a bigger miracle than Velikovsky's principal collisional thesis. Velikovsky makes (page 187) a lame aside on the "ability of many small insects . . . to live in an atmosphere devoid of oxygen," which misses the point. The question is how an organism that evolved on Jupiter could live in and metabolize an atmosphere rich in oxygen.

Next there is the problem of fly ablation. Small flies have just the same mass and dimensions as small meteors, which are burned up at an altitude of about 100 kilometers when they enter the Earth's atmosphere on cometary trajectories. Ablation accounts for the visibility of such meteors. Not only would cometary vermin be transformed rapidly into fried flies on entrance into the Earth's atmosphere; they would then be, as cometary meteors would be today, vaporized into atoms and never "swarm" over Egypt to the consternation of the Pharoah. Likewise, the temperatures attendant to ejection of the comet from Jupiter, referred to above, would fry Velikovsky's flies. Impossible to begin with, doubly fried and atomized, cometary flies do not well survive critical scrutiny.

Finally, there is a curious reference to intelligent extraterrestrial life in *Worlds in Collision.* On page 364, Velikovsky argues that the near collisions of Mars with the Earth and Venus "make it highly improbable that any higher forms of life, if they previously existed there, survived on Mars." But when we examine Mars as seen by Mariner 9, we find that a bit more than one-third of the planet has a modified cratered terrain somewhat reminiscent of the moon and that it shows no sign of spectacular catastrophes other than ancient impacts. The other one-half to two-thirds of the planet shows many fewer signs of such impacts, but instead displays dramatic signs of major tectonic activity, lava flows, and volcanism several hundred million years ago. The small but detectable amount of impact cratering in this terrain shows that it was made much longer than several thousand years ago. There is no way to reconcile this picture with a view of a planet recently so devastated by impact catastrophism that all intelligent life would thereby have been eliminated. It is also by no means clear why, if all life on Mars were to be exterminated in such encounters, all life on Earth was not similarly exterminated.

PROBLEM VI. MANNA

Manna, according to the etymology in *Exodus,* derives from the Hebrew words *man-hu,* which mean "What is it?" Indeed, an excellent question! The idea of food falling from comets is not absolutely straightforward. Optical spectroscopy of comet tails, even before *Worlds in Collision* was published in 1950, showed the presence of simple fragments of hydrocarbons; but no aldehydes—the building blocks of carbohydrates—were known then or have been found subsequently. They may nevertheless be present in comets. However, from the recent passage of Comet Kohoutek near the Earth, it is now known that comets contain large quantities of simple nitriles—in particular, hydrogen cyanide and methyl cyanide. These are poisons, and it is not immediately obvious that comets are good to eat.

But let us put this objection aside, grant Velikovsky his hypothesis, and calculate the consequences. How much manna is required to feed the hundreds of thousands of Children of Israel for forty years (see *Exodus* 16:35)?

In *Exodus* 16:20, we find that the manna left overnight was infested by bread worms in the morning—an event possible with carbohydrates but extremely unlikely with hydrocarbons. (Moses, however, may have been a better chemist than Velikovsky.) This event also shows that manna was not storable. It fell every day for forty years according to the Biblical account. We will assume that the quantity which fell every day was just sufficient to feed the Children of Israel, although Velikovsky assures us (page 138) from midrashic sources that the quantity which fell was adequate for two thousand years rather than a mere forty. Let us assume that each Israelite ate on the order of one-third of a kilogram of manna per day, somewhat less than a subsistence diet. Then each will eat 100 kilograms per year and 4,000 kilograms in forty years. Hundreds of thousands of Israelites, the number explicitly mentioned in *Exodus*, will then consume something over a million kg of manna during the forty years wandering in the desert. But we cannot imagine the debris from the cometary tail falling each day* preferentially on the portion of the Wilderness of Sin in which the Israelites happened to have wandered. This would be no less miraculous than the Biblical account taken at face value. The area occupied by a few hundred thousand itinerant tribesmen, wandering under a common leadership, is, very roughly, several times 10^{-7} the area

* Actually, according to *Exodus,* manna fell each day except on the Sabbath. A double ration, uninfected by bread worms, fell instead on Friday. This seems awkward for Velikovsky's hypothesis. How could the comet know? Indeed, this raises a general problem about Velikovsky's historical method. Some quotations from his religious and historical sources are to be taken literally; others are to be dismissed as "local embellishments." But what is the standard by which this decision is made? Surely such a standard must involve a criterion independent of our predispositions to Velikovsky's contentions.

of the Earth. Therefore, during the forty years of wandering, the whole Earth must have accumulated several times 10^{18} gm of manna, or enough to cover the entire surface of the planet with manna to a depth of about an inch. If this indeed happened, it would certainly be a memorable event, and may even account for the gingerbread house in *Hansel and Gretel.* But now there is no reason for the manna to have fallen only on the Earth. In forty years, the tail of the comet, if restricted to the inner solar system, would have traversed some 10^{10} km. Making only a modest allowance for the ratio of the volume of the Earth to the volume of the tail, we find that the mass of manna distributed to the inner solar system by this event is larger than 10^{28} gm. This is not only more massive by many orders of magnitude than the most massive comet known; it is already more massive than the planet Venus. But comets cannot be composed only of manna. (Indeed, no manna at all has been detected so far in comets.) Comets are known to be composed primarily of ices, and a conservative estimate of the ratio of the mass of the comet to the mass of the manna is much larger than 10^3. Therefore, the mass of the comet must be much larger than 10^{31} gm. This is the mass of Jupiter. If we were to accept Velikovsky's midrashic source above, we would deduce that the comet had a mass comparable to that of the sun. Interplanetary space in the inner solar system should even today be filled with manna. I leave it to the reader to make his own judgment on the validity of Velikovsky's hypothesis in the light of such calculations.

PROBLEM VII. THE CLOUDS OF VENUS

Velikovsky's prognostication that the clouds of Venus were made of carbohydrates has many times been hailed as an example of a successful scientific prediction. From Velikovsky's general thesis and the calculations just described above, it is clear that Venus should be saturated with manna. Indeed, Velikovsky says (page x) that "the presence of hydrocarbon gases and dust in the cloud envelope of Venus would constitute a crucial test" for his ideas. We see here another example of his confusion between hydrocarbons and carbohydrates. It is also not clear whether "dust" in the foregoing quotation refers to hydrocarbon dust or just ordinary silicate dust. On the same page, Velikovsky quotes himself as saying, "On the basis of this research, I assume that Venus must be rich in petroleum gases"; which seems to be an unambiguous reference to the components of natural gas, such as methane, ethane, ethylene, and acetylene.

At this point, a little history must enter our story. In the 1930's and early 1940's, the only astronomer in the world concerning himself with planetary chemistry was the late Rupert Wildt, once of Göttingen, and later at Yale. It was Wildt who first identified methane in the atmospheres of Jupiter and Saturn, and it was he who first proposed the presence of higher hydrocarbon gases in the atmospheres of these planets. Thus, the idea that "petroleum gases" might exist on Jupiter is not original with Velikovsky. Likewise, it was Wildt who proposed that formaldehyde might be a constituent of the atmosphere of Venus, and that a carbohydrate polymer of formaldehyde might constitute the clouds. The idea of carbohydrates in the clouds of Venus was not original with Velikovsky either, and it is difficult to believe that one who so thoroughly researched the astronomical literature of the 1930's and 1940's was unaware of these papers by Wildt which relate so closely to Velikovsky's central theme. Yet, there is no mention whatever of the Jupiter phase of Wildt's work and only a footnote on formaldehyde (page 368), without references, and without any acknowledgment that Wildt had proposed carbohydrates on Venus. Wildt, unlike Velikovsky, understood well the difference between hydrocarbons and carbohydrates; moreover, he performed unsuccessful spectroscopic searches in the near-ultraviolet for the proposed formaldehyde monomer. Being unable to find the monomer, Wildt (1942) abandoned the hypothesis. Velikovsky did not.

As I pointed out many years ago (Sagan, 1961), the vapor pressure of simple hydrocarbons in the vicinity of the clouds of Venus should make them detectable if they comprise the clouds. They were not detectable then, and in the intervening years, despite the use of a wide range of analytic techniques, neither hydrocarbons nor carbohydrates have been detected. These molecules have been searched for by high-resolution ground-based optical spectroscopy, including Fourier transform techniques; by ultraviolet spectroscopy from the Wisconsin Experimental Package of the Orbiting Astronomical Observatory OAO-2; by ground-based infrared observations; and by direct entry probes of the Soviet Union. Not one of them has been found. Typical abundance upper limits on the simplest hydrocarbons and on aldehydes, the building blocks of carbohydrates, are a few parts per million (Connes et al., 1967; Owen and Sagan, 1972). (The corresponding upper limits for Mars are also a few parts per million [Owen and Sagan, 1972].) All observations are consistent in showing that the bulk of the Venus atmosphere is composed of carbon dioxide. Indeed, because the carbon is present in such an oxidized form, at best trace constituents of the simple reduced hydrocarbons could be expected. Observations on the wings of the critical 3.5μ region show not the slightest trace of the C-H absorption feature common to both hydrocarbons and carbohydrates (Pollack et al., 1974). All other absorption bands in the Venus spectrum, from the ultraviolet through the infrared, are now understood; none of them is due to hydrocarbons or carbohydrates. No specific organic molecule has ever been suggested which can explain with precision the infrared spectrum of Venus, as it is now known.

Moreover, the question of the composition of the Venus clouds—a major enigma for centuries—has recently been solved (Young and Young, 1973; Sill, 1972; Young, 1973; Pollack et al., 1974). The clouds of Venus are composed of an approximately 75 percent solution of sulfuric acid. This identification is consistent with the chemistry of the Venus atmosphere, in which hydrofluoric and hydrocholoric acid have also been found; with the real part of the refractive index, deduced from polarimetry, which is known to three significant figures (1.44); with the 11.2μ and 3μ (and, now, far infrared) absorption features; and with the discontinuity in the abundance of water vapor above and below the clouds. These observed features are inconsistent with the hypothesis of hydrocarbon or carbohydrate clouds.

With such organic clouds now so thoroughly discredited, why do we hear about space-vehicle research having corroborated Velikovsky's thesis? This also requires a story. On December 14, 1962, the first successful American interplanetary spacecraft, Mariner 2, flew by Venus. Built by the Jet Propulsion Laboratory, it carried, among other more important instruments, an infrared radiometer for which I happened to be one of four experimenters. This was at a time before the first successful flight of the lunar Ranger spacecraft, and NASA was comparatively inexperienced in releasing the scientific findings. A press conference was held in Washington to announce the results, and L. D. Kaplan, one of the experimenters on our team, was delegated to describe the results to the assembled reporters. It is clear that when his time came, he described the results with somewhat the following flavor (these are not his exact words): "Our experiment was a two-channel infrared radiometer, one channel centered in the 10.4 micron CO_2 hot band; the other in an 8.4 micron clear window in the gas phase of the Venus atmosphere. The objective was to measure absolute brightness temperatures and differential transmission between the two channels. A limb-darkening law was found in which the normalized intensity varied as mu to the power alpha, where mu is the arccosine of the angle between the local planetary normal and the line of sight, and. . . ." At some such point, he was interrupted by impatient reporters, unused to the intricacies of science, who said something like, "Don't tell us the dull stuff; give us the real poop! How thick are the clouds, how high are they, and what are they made of?" Kaplan replied, quite properly, that the infrared radiometer experiment was not designed to test such questions nor did it. But then he said something like, "I'll tell you what I think." He then went on to describe his view that the greenhouse effect, needed to keep the surface of Venus hot (see below), might not work on Venus because the atmospheric constituents seemed to be transparent at a wavelength in the vicinity of 3.5μ. If some absorber at this wavelength existed in the Venus atmosphere, the window could be plugged, the greenhouse effect retained, and the high surface temperature accounted for. He proposed that hydrocarbons would be splendid greenhouse molecules.

Kaplan's cautions were not noted by the press, and the next day headlines could be found in many American newspapers saying, "Hydrocarbon Clouds Found on Venus by Mariner 2." Meanwhile, back at the Jet Propulsion Laboratory, a group of Laboratory publicists were in the process of writing a popular report on the mission, since called "Mariner: Mission to Venus." One imagines them in the midst of writing, picking up the morning newspaper and saying, "Hey! I didn't know we found hydrocarbon clouds on Venus." And, indeed, that publication (Wheelock, 1963) lists hydrocarbon clouds as one of the principal discoveries of Mariner 2: "At their base, the clouds are about 200 degrees F and probably are comprised of condensed hydrocarbons held in oily suspension." (The report also opts for greenhouse heating of the Venus surface, but Velikovsky has chosen to believe only a part of what was printed.)

One now imagines the Administrator of NASA passing on the good tidings to the President in the annual report of the Space Administration; the President handing it on yet another step in his annual report to Congress; and the writers of elementary astronomy texts, always anxious to include the very latest results, enshrining this "finding" in their pages. With so many apparently reliable, high-level, and mutually consistent reports that Mariner 2 found hydrocarbon clouds on Venus, it is no wonder that Velikovsky and several fair-minded scientists, inexperienced in the mysterious ways of NASA, might deduce that here is the classic test of a scientific theory: an apparently bizarre prediction, made before the observation, and then unexpectedly confirmed by observation.

The true situation is very different, as we have seen. Neither Mariner 2 nor any subsequent investigation of the Venus atmosphere has found evidence for hydrocarbons or carbohydrates, in gas, liquid, or solid phase. It is now known (Pollack, 1969) that carbon dioxide and water vapor adequately fill the 3.5 micron window. It is ironic that the Mariner 2 "argument" for hydrocarbon clouds on Venus in fact derives from an attempt to rescue the greenhouse explanation of the high surface temperature, which Velikovsky does not support. It is also ironic that Kaplan was later co-author of a paper which set a very sensitive upper limit on the abundance of methane, a "petroleum gas," in a spectroscopic examination of the Venus atmosphere (Connes et al., 1967).

In summary, Velikovsky's idea that the clouds of Venus are composed of hydrocarbons or carbohydrates is neither original nor correct. The "crucial test" fails.

PROBLEM VIII. THE TEMPERATURE OF VENUS

Another curious circumstance concerns the surface temperature of Venus. While the high temperature of Venus is often quoted as a successful prediction and a support of Velikovsky's hypothesis, the reasoning behind his conclusion and the consequences of his arguments do not seem to be widely known nor discussed.

Let us begin by considering Velikovsky's views on the temperature of Mars (pages 367–368). He believes that Mars, being a relatively small planet, was more severely affected in its encounters with the more massive Venus and Earth, and, therefore, that Mars should have a high temperature. He proposes that the mechanism may be "a conversion of motion into heat," which is a little vague since heat is precisely the motion of molecules; or, much more fantastic, by "interplanetary electrical discharges" which "could also initiate atomic fissions with ensuing radioactivity and emission of heat."

Velikovsky, in the same section, baldly states, "Mars emits more heat than it receives from the sun," in apparent consistency with his collision hypothesis. This statement is, however, dead wrong. The temperature of Mars has been measured repeatedly by Soviet and American spacecraft and by ground-based observers, and the temperatures of all parts of Mars are just what is calculated from the amount of sunlight absorbed by the surface. What is more, this was well known in the 1940's, before Velikovsky's book was published. And while he mentions four prominent scientists who were involved before 1950 in measuring the temperature of Mars, he makes no reference to their work and explicitly and erroneously states that they concluded that Mars gave off more radiation than it received from the sun.

It is difficult to understand this set of errors, and the most generous hypothesis I can offer is that Velikovsky confused the visible part of the electromagnetic spectrum, in which sunlight heats Mars, with the infrared part of the spectrum, in which Mars largely radiates to space. But the conclusion is clear. Mars, even more than Venus, by Velikovsky's argument should be a "hot planet." Had Mars proved to be unexpectedly hot, perhaps we would have heard of this as a further confirmation of Velikovsky's views. But when Mars turns out to have exactly the temperature everyone expected it to have, we do not hear of this as a refutation of Velikovsky's views. There is a planetary double standard at work.

When we now move on to Venus, we find rather similar arguments brought into play. I find it odd that Velikovsky does not attribute the temperature of Venus to its ejection from Jupiter (see Problem I, above); but he does not. Instead, we are told, because of its close encounter with the Earth and Mars, that Venus must have been heated; but also (page 77) "the head of the comet . . . had passed close to the sun and was in a state of candescence." Then, when the comet became the planet Venus, it must still have been "very hot" and have "given off heat" (page ix). Again, the pre-1950 astronomical observations are referred to (page 370), which show that the dark side of Venus is approximately as hot as the bright side of Venus, to the level probed by middle-infrared radiation. Here Velikovsky accurately quotes the astronomical investigators, and from their work deduces (page 371) "the night side of Venus radiates heat because Venus is hot." Of course!

What I think Velikovsky is trying to say here is that his Venus, like his Mars, is giving off more heat than it receives from the sun, and that the observed temperatures on both the night and day sides are due more to the "candescence" of Venus than to the radiation it now receives from the sun. But this is a serious error. The bolometric albedo of Venus is about 0.73, entirely consistent with the observed infrared temperature of the clouds of Venus of about 240°K; that is to say, the clouds of Venus are precisely at the temperature expected on the basis of the amount of sunlight which is absorbed there.

Velikovsky proposed that both Venus and Mars give off more heat than they receive from the sun. He is wrong for both planets. Jupiter was suggested by Gerard Kuiper (1949) to give off more heat than it receives, and subsequent observations have proved him right. But, of this, *Worlds in Collision* breathes not a word.

Velikovsky proposed that Venus is hot because of its encounters with Mars and the Earth, and its close passage to the sun. Since Mars is not anomalously hot, the high surface temperature of Venus must then be attributed primarily to the passage of Venus near the sun during its cometary incarnation. But it is easy to calculate how much energy Venus would have received during its close passage to the sun and how long it would take for this energy to be radiated away into space. This calculation is performed in Appendix 3 where we find that all of this energy is lost in a period of months to years after the close passage to the sun, and that there is no chance of any of that heat being retained at the present time in Velikovsky's chronology. Velikovsky does not mention how close to the sun Venus is supposed to have passed, but a very close passage compounds the already extremely grave collision-physics difficulties outlined in Appendix 1. Incidentally, there is a slight hint in *Worlds in Collision* that Velikovsky believes that comets shine by emitted rather than reflected light. If so, this may be the source of some of his confusion regarding Venus.

Velikovsky nowhere states the temperature he believed Venus to be at in 1950. On page 77 he says vaguely that the comet that later became Venus was in a state of "candescence," but in the preface of the 1965 edition of *Worlds in Collision* (page xi) Velikovsky claims to have predicted "an incandescent state of

Venus." This is not nearly the same thing—because of the rapid cooling after its supposed solar encounter (Appendix 3). Moreover, Velikovsky himself is proposing that Venus is cooling through time; so what precisely Velikovsky meant by saying that Venus is "hot" is to some degree obscure.

Velikovsky writes in the 1965 preface that his claim of a high surface temperature was "in total disagreement with what was known in 1946." This turns out to be not quite the case. The dominant figure of Rupert Wildt again looms over the astronomical side of Velikovsky's hypothesis. Wildt, who, unlike Velikovsky, understood the nature of the problem, predicted correctly that Venus and not Mars would be "hot." In a 1940 paper in the *Astrophysical Journal,* Wildt argued that the surface of Venus was much hotter than conventional astronomical opinion had held, because of a carbon-dioxide greenhouse effect. Carbon dioxide had recently been discovered spectroscopically in the atmosphere of Venus, and Wildt correctly pointed out that the observed large quantity of CO_2 would trap infrared radiation given off by the surface of the planet, until the surface temperature rose to a higher value so that the incoming visible sunlight just balanced the outgoing infrared planetary emission. Wildt calculated that the temperature would be almost 400°K, or around the normal boiling point of water (373°K = 212°F = 100°C). There is no doubt that this was the most careful treatment of the surface temperature of Venus prior to the 1950's, and it is again odd that Velikovsky, who seems to have read all papers on Venus and Mars published in the *Astrophysical Journal* in the 1920's, 1930's, and 1940's, somehow overlooked this historically significant work.

We now know from ground-based radio observations and from the remarkably successful direct entry and landing probes of the Soviet Union that the surface temperature of Venus is within a few degrees of 750°K (Marov, 1972). The surface atmospheric pressure is about 90 times that at the surface of the Earth, and is comprised primarily of carbon dioxide. This large abundance of carbon dioxide, plus the smaller quantities of water vapor which have been detected on Venus, are adequate to heat the surface to the observed temperature via the greenhouse effect. The Venera 8 descent module, the first spacecraft to land on the illuminated hemisphere of Venus, found it light at the surface, and the Soviet experimenters concluded that the amount of light reaching the surface and the atmospheric constitution were together adequate to drive the required radiative-convective greenhouse (Marov et al., 1973). These results were confirmed by the Venera 9 and 10 missions, which obtained clear photographs in sunlight of surface rocks. Velikovsky thus is certainly mistaken when he says (page ix) that "light does not penetrate the cloud cover"; and is probably mistaken when he says (page ix) that the "greenhouse effect could not explain so high a temperature."

A repeated claim by Velikovsky is that Venus is cooling off with time. Its high temperature, we have seen, he attributes to solar heating during a close solar passage. In many publications Velikovsky compares published temperature measurements of Venus, made at different times, and tries to show the desired cooling. An unbiased presentation of the microwave brightness temperatures of Venus—the only nonspacecraft data which apply to the surface temperature of the planet—are exhibited in Figure 1 below. The error bars represent the uncertainties in the measurement processes as estimated by the radio observers themselves. We see that there is not the faintest hint of a decline in temperature with time (if anything, there is a suggestion of an increase with time, but the error bars are sufficiently large that such a conclusion is also unsupported by the data). Similar results apply to measurements, in the infrared part of the spectrum, of cloud temperatures: they are lower in magnitude and do not decline with time. Moreover, the simplest considerations of the solution of the one-dimensional equation of heat conduction show that in the Velikovskian scenario essentially all the cooling by radiation to space would have occurred long ago. Even if Velikovsky were right about the source of the high Venus surface temperatures, his prediction of a secular temperature decrease would be erroneous.

The high surface temperature of Venus is another of the so-

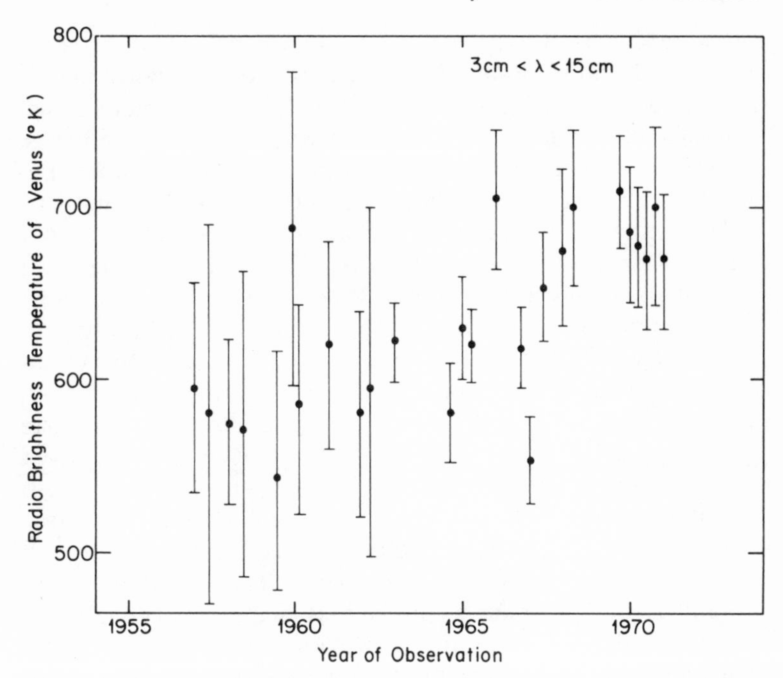

Figure 1. Microwave brightness temperatures of Venus as a function of time. There is certainly no evidence of a declining surface temperature. The wavelength of observation is denoted by λ. (This figure, prepared by David Morrison, appears also in Morrison's chapter, page 163 below.)

called "proofs" of the Velikovsky hypothesis. We find (1) that the temperature in question was never specified; (2) that the mechanism proposed for providing this temperature is grossly inadequate; (3) that the surface of the planet does not cool off with time as advertised; and (4) that the idea of a high surface temperature on Venus was published in the dominant astronomical journal of its time and with an essentially correct argument ten years before the publication of *Worlds in Collision*.

PROBLEM IX. THE CRATERS OF VENUS

In 1973 an important aspect of the surface of Venus was discovered by Richard Goldstein and associates, using the Goldstone radar observatory of the Jet Propulsion Laboratory. Goldstein et al. found, from radar which penetrates Venus' clouds and is reflected off its surface, that the planet is cratered, and, perhaps, like parts of the moon, is saturation-cratered—that is, so packed with craters that one crater overlaps the other. Because successive volcanic eruptions tend to use the same lava tube, saturation cratering is a characteristic of impact rather than volcanic cratering mechanisms. This is not a conclusion predicted by Velikovsky, but that is not my point. These craters, like the craters in the lunar maria, on Mercury, and in the cratered regions of Mars, are produced almost exclusively by impact of interplanetary debris. Large crater-forming objects will not be dissipated as they enter the Venus atmosphere, despite its high density. Now the colliding objects cannot have arrived at Venus in the last ten thousand years; otherwise, the Earth would be as plentifully cratered. The most likely source of these collisions is the asteroids which cross the Earth's orbit, called Apollo objects, and the small comets which are discussed in Appendix 1. But for them to produce as many craters as Venus possesses, the cratering process on Venus must have taken billions of years. Alternatively, the cratering may have occurred more rapidly in the very earliest history of the solar system. But there is no way for it to have happened recently. On the other hand, if Venus was, thirty-five hundred years ago, in the deep interior of Jupiter, there is no way it could have accumulated such impacts there. The clear conclusion from the craters of Venus is, therefore, that Venus has been for billions of years an object exposed to interplanetary collisions—in direct contradiction to the fundamental premise of Velikovsky's hypothesis.

The Venus craters are significantly eroded. Some of the rocks on the surface of the planet, as revealed by the Venera 9 and 10 photography, are quite young; others are severely eroded. Possible mechanisms for erosion on the Venus surface—including chemical weathering and slow deformation at high temperatures—are described elsewhere (Sagan, 1976). However, these findings have no bearing whatever on the Velikovskian hypotheses: recent volcanic activity on Venus need no more be attributed to a close passage to the sun, or to Venus being in some vague sense a "young" planet, than would recent volcanic activity on Earth.

Velikovsky (1967) wrote: "Obviously, if the planet is billions of years old, it could not have preserved its original heat; also, any radioactive process that can produce such heat must be of a very rapid decay [*sic*], and this again would not square with an age of the planet counted in billions of years." Unfortunately, Velikovsky has failed to understand two classic and basic geophysical results. Thermal conduction is a much slower process than radiation or convection, and, in the case of the Earth, primordial heat makes a detectable contribution to the geothermal temperature gradient and to the heat flux from the Earth's interior. The same applies to Venus. Also, the radionuclides responsible for radioactive heating of the Earth's crust are long-lived isotopes of uranium, thorium, and potassium—isotopes with half-lives comparable to the age of the planet. Again, the same applies to Venus.

PROBLEM X. THE CIRCULARIZATION OF THE ORBIT OF VENUS AND NONGRAVITATIONAL FORCES IN THE SOLAR SYSTEM

The idea that Venus could have been converted, in a few thousand years, from an object in a highly eccentric orbit to its present orbit, which is, except for Neptune, the most nearly perfect circular orbit of all the planets, is at odds with what we know about the three-body problem in celestial mechanics. However, it must be admitted that this is not a completely solved problem, and that, while the odds are large, they are not absolutely overwhelming, against Velikovsky's hypothesis on this score. Furthermore, when Velikovsky invokes electrical or magnetic forces, with no effort to calculate their magnitude or describe in detail their effects, we are hard-pressed to assess his ideas. However, simple arguments from the required magnetic energy density to circularize a comet's orbit show that the field strengths implied are unreasonably high (Appendix 4)—they are counterindicated by studies of rock magnetization.

We can also approach the problem empirically. Straightforward Newtonian mechanics is able to predict with remarkable accuracy the trajectories of spacecraft, so that, for example, Mariner 9 was placed within 100 kilometers of its designated orbit; Venera 8 was placed precisely on the sunlit side of the equatorial terminator of Venus; and Pioneer 10 was placed in exactly the correct entry corridor in the vicinity of Jupiter to be expelled from the solar system. No mysterious electrical or magnetic influences were encountered. Newtonian mechanics is adequate to predict, with great precision, for example, the exact moment when the Galilean satellites of Jupiter will eclipse each other.

Comets, it is true, have somewhat less predictable orbits; but this is almost certainly due to the boiling off of frozen ices as these objects approach the sun, and to a small rocket effect. The cometary incarnation of Venus, if it existed, might also have had such icy vaporization; but there is no way in which the rocket effect would have preferentially brought that comet into close passages with the Earth or Mars. Halley's comet, which has been observed probably for two thousand years, remains on a highly eccentric orbit and has not shown the slightest tendency toward circularization; yet it is almost as old as Velikovsky's "comet." It is extraordinarily unlikely that Velikovsky's comet, had it ever existed, became the planet Venus.

Some Other Problems

These preceding ten points are the major scientific flaws in Velikovsky's argument, as nearly as I can determine. I have discussed earlier in this chapter some of the difficulties with his approach to ancient writings. Let me here list a few of the miscellaneous other problems that I have encountered in reading *Worlds in Collision*.

On page 280, the Martian moons Phobos and Deimos are imagined to have "snatched some of Mars' atmosphere" and to thereby appear very bright. But it is immediately clear that the escape velocity on these objects—perhaps 20 miles per hour—is so small as to make them incapable of retaining even temporarily any atmosphere; and they are among the darkest objects in the solar system.

Beginning on page 281, there is a comparison of the Biblical Book of *Joel* and a set of Vedic hymns describing "Maruts." Velikovsky believes that the "Maruts" were a host of meteorites which preceded and followed Mars during its close approach to the Earth, which he also believes to be described in *Joel.* Velikovsky says (page 286) "Joel did not copy from the *Vedas* nor the *Vedas* from Joel." Yet, on page 288, Velikovsky finds it "gratifying" to discover that the words "Mars" and "Marut" are cognates. But how, if the stories in *Joel* and the *Vedas* are independent, could the two words possibly be cognates?

On page 307, we find Isaiah making an accurate prediction of the time of the return of Mars for another collision with the Earth "based on experience during previous perturbations." If so, Isaiah must have been able to solve the full three-body problem with electrical and magnetic forces thrown in, and it is a pity that this knowledge was not also passed down to us in the Old Testament.

On pages 366 and 367 we find an argument that Venus, Mars, and the Earth, in their interactions, must have exchanged atmospheres. If massive quantities of terrestrial molecular oxygen (20 percent of our atmosphere) were transferred to Mars and Venus thirty-five hundred years ago, they should be there still in massive amounts. The time scale for turnover of O_2 in the Earth's atmosphere is two thousand years, and that is by a biological process. In the absence of abundant biological respiration, any O_2 on Mars and Venus thirty-five hundred years ago should still be there. Yet we know quite definitely from spectroscopy that O_2 is at best a tiny constituent of the already extremely thin Martian atmosphere (and is likewise scarce on Venus). Mariner 10 found evidence of oxygen in the atmosphere of Venus: but tiny quantities of atomic oxygen in the upper atmosphere, not massive quantities of molecular oxygen in the lower atmosphere. The dearth of O_2 on Venus also renders untenable Velikovsky's belief in petroleum fires in the lower Venus atmosphere—neither the fuel nor the oxidant is present in appreciable amounts. These fires, Velikovsky believed, would produce water, which would be photodissociated, yielding atomic oxygen (O). Thus, Velikovsky requires significant deep atmospheric O_2 to account for upper atmospheric O. In fact, the O found is understood very well in terms of the photochemical breakdown of the principal atmospheric constituent, CO_2, into CO and O. These distinctions seem to have been lost on some of Velikovsky's supporters, who seized on the Mariner 10 findings as a vindication of *Worlds in Collison*.

Since there is negligible oxygen and water vapor in the Martian atmosphere, Velikovsky argues, some other constituent of the Martian atmosphere must be derived from Earth. The argument, unfortunately, is a *non sequitur*. Velikovsky opts for argon and neon, despite the fact that these are quite rare constituents of the Earth's atmosphere. The first published argument for argon and neon as major constituents of the Martian atmosphere was made by Harrison Brown in the 1940's. Substantial quantities of neon are now excluded by the Mariner 9 S-band occultation experiment. But even if large quantities of argon are found on Mars, it would be no evidence for a Velikovskian atmospheric exchange, because the most abundant form of argon, Ar^{40}, is produced by the radioactive decay of potassium 40, which is expected in the crust of Mars.* A much more serious problem for Velikovsky is the apparent absence of N_2 (nitrogen molecules) from the Martian atmosphere. The gas is relatively unreactive, does not freeze out at Martian temperatures, and cannot rapidly escape from the Martian exosphere. It is the major constituent of the Earth's atmosphere. If such an exchange of gases occurred, where is the N_2 on Mars? These tests of the assumed gas exchange between Mars and Earth, which Velikovsky advocates, are poorly thought out in his writings; in fact, the tests contradict his thesis.

* [Editor's note: The Viking landings on Mars in 1976 determined once again that the Martian atmosphere consists mainly of carbon dioxide. Ar^{40} forms about 2 percent of the atmosphere, while the amount of neon is several orders of magnitude less.]

Conclusions

Worlds in Collision is an attempt to validate Biblical and other folklore as history if not theology. I have tried to approach the book with no prejudgments. I find the mythological concordances fascinating and worth further investigation; but they are probably explicable on diffusionist or other grounds. The scientific part of the text, despite all the claims of "proofs," runs into at least ten distinct and very grave difficulties.

Of the ten tests of Velikovsky's work described above, there is not one case where his ideas are simultaneously original and consistent with simple physical theory and observation. Moreover, many of the objections—especially those set forth in Problems I, II, III, and X—are objections of high weight, based on the motion and conservation laws of physics. In science, an acceptable argument must show a clear chain of evidence. If a single link in the chain is broken, the argument fails. In the case of *Worlds in Collision,* we have the opposite: virtually every link in the chain is broken. To rescue the hypothesis requires special pleading, the vague invention of new physics, and selective inattention to a plethora of conflicting evidence. Accordingly, Velikovsky's basic thesis seems to me clearly untenable on physical grounds.

Moreover, there is a dangerous potential problem with the mythological material. The supposed events are reconstructed from legends and folk tales. But these global catastrophes are not clearly presented in the historical records of many peoples. Such strange omissions are accounted for, when they are noted at all, by "collective amnesia." Velikovsky wants it both ways. Where concordances exist, he is prepared to draw the most sweeping conclusions from them. Where concordances do not exist, the difficulty is dismissed by invoking "collective amnesia." With so lax a standard of evidence, anything can be "proved."

I should also point out that a perfectly plausible alternative explanation exists for most of the events recorded in *Exodus,* an alternative that is much more in accord with physics. The Exodus is dated in *I Kings* as occurring four hundred and eighty years before the initiation of the construction of the Temple of Solomon. With other supporting calculations, the date for the Biblical *Exodus* is then computed to be about 1447 B.C. (Covey, 1975). But this is astonishingly close to dates obtained by a variety of scientific methods for the final and colossal volcanic explosion of the island of Thera (or Santorin) which may have destroyed the Minoan civilization in Crete, and which clearly had profound consequences in Egypt, five hundred miles to the South. The best available radiocarbon date for the event, obtained from a tree buried in volcanic ash on Thera, is 1456 B.C., with an error in the method of at least plus or minus forty-three years. The amount of volcanic dust produced is more than adequate to account for three days of darkness in daytime, and accompanying events can account for earthquakes, famine, vermin, and a range of familiar Velikovskian catastrophes. It also produced an immense Mediterranean tsunami or tidal wave, which Angelos Galanopoulos (1964), who is responsible for much of the recent geological and archeological interest in Thera, believes can account for the parting of the Red Sea as well. (An informative and entertaining discussion of the Thera case, and the whole question of the connection of myth with geological events, can be found in the book by Dorothy Vitaliano [1973]. See, also, L. Sprague de Camp [1975].) In a certain sense, the Galanopoulos explanation of the events in *Exodus* is even more provocative than Velikovsky's explanation, because Galanopoulos has presented moderately convincing evidence that Thera corresponds in almost all essential details to the legendary civilization of Atlantis. If he is right, it is the destruction of Atlantis rather than the apparition of a comet which permitted the Israelites to leave Egypt.

There are many strange inconsistencies in *Worlds in Collision,* some of which we have already mentioned. But on the next to last page of the book, a breathtaking departure from the fundamental thesis is casually introduced. Here we read of a hoary and erroneous analogy between the structures of solar systems and of atoms. Suddenly, we are presented with the hypothesis that the supposed errant motions of the planets, rather than being the result of collisions, are instead due to changes in the quantum energy levels of planets attendant to the absorption of a photon—or perhaps several. Solar systems are held together by gravitational forces; atoms by electrical forces. While both forces depend on the inverse square of distance they have totally different characters and magnitudes: as one of many differences, there are positive and negative electrical charges, but only one sign of gravitational mass. We understand both solar systems and atoms well enough to see that Velikovsky's proposed "quantum jumps" of planets are based on a misunderstanding of both theories and evidence.

To the best of my knowledge, there is not a single astronomical prediction correctly made in *Worlds in Collision* with sufficient precision for it to be more than a vague lucky guess; and there are, as I have tried to point out, a host of claims made which are demonstrably false. The existence of strong radio emission from Jupiter is sometimes pointed to as the most striking example of a correct prediction by Velikovsky; but all objects give off radio waves if they are at temperatures above absolute zero. The essential character of the Jovian radio emission—that it is nonthermal, polarized, intermittent radiation, connected with the vast belts of charged particles which surround Jupiter, trapped by its strong magnetic field—are nowhere predicted by Velikovsky. Indeed, his "prediction" is clearly not linked in its essentials to the fundamental Velikovskian theses.

Merely guessing something right does not necessarily demonstrate prior knowledge or a correct theory. For example, in an early science fiction work dated 1949, Max Erhlich imagined a near collision of the Earth with another cosmic object which filled the sky and terrorized the inhabitants of the Earth. Most frightening was the fact that there was on this passing planet a natural feature which looked very much like a huge eye. This is one of many fictional and serious antecedents to Velikovsky's idea that such collisions happen frequently. But that is not my point. In a recent discussion of how it is that the side of the moon which faces the Earth has large smooth maria while the averted face of the moon is almost free of maria, John Wood of the Smithsonian Astrophysical Observatory proposed that the side of the moon now turned toward the Earth was once at the edge or limb of the moon, on the leading hemisphere of the moon's motion about the Earth. In this position it swept up, billions of years ago, a ring of debris which surrounded the Earth and which may have been involved in the formation of the earth-moon system. By Euler's laws, the moon must then have altered its rotation axis to correspond to its new principal moment of inertia, so that the leading hemisphere then faced the Earth. The remarkable conclusion is that there would have been a time, according to Wood, when what is now the eastern limb of the moon would have been facing the Earth. But the eastern limb of the moon has an enormous collision feature, billions of years old, called Mare Orientale, which looks very much like a giant eye. No one suggests that Ehrlich was relying upon a racial memory of an event three billion years ago when he wrote *The Big Eye*. It is merely a coincidence. When enough fiction is written and enough scientific hypotheses proposed, sooner or later there will be accidental concordances.

With these enormous liabilities, how is it that *Worlds in Collision* has been so popular? Here I can only guess. For one thing, it is an attempted validation of religion. The old Biblical stories are literally true, Velikovsky tells us, if only we interpret them in the right way. The Jewish people, for example, saved from Egyptian Pharoahs, Assyrian kings, and innumerable other disasters by obliging cometary interventions, had every right to believe themselves chosen. Velikovsky attempts to rescue not only religion, but also astrology: the outcomes of wars, the fates of whole peoples, are determined by the positions of the planets. In some sense, his work holds out a promise of the cosmic connectedness of mankind—a sentiment with which I sympathize, but in a somewhat different context (see Sagan, 1973)—and the reassurance that ancient peoples and other cultures were not so very dumb after all.

The outrage which seems to have seized many otherwise placid scientists upon colliding with *Worlds in Collision* has produced a chain of consequences. Some young people are put off by the occasional pomposity of scientists; or are concerned by what they apprehend as the dangers of science and technology; or perhaps merely have difficulty understanding science. They may take some comfort in seeing scientists get their lumps.

To the extent that scientists have not given Velikovsky the reasoned response his work calls for, we have ourselves been responsible for the propagation of Velikovskian confusion. But scientists cannot attempt to deal with all areas of borderline science, of which the number is legion in America today. The thinking, calculation, and preparation of this chapter, for example, took badly needed time away from my own research. But it was certainly not boring, and at the very least I had a brush with many an enjoyable legend. I hope that in the future Velikovsky's views and the views of other popular proponents of borderline science will receive a reasoned, if hopefully briefer, scientific response.

The attempt to rescue old-time religion, in an age which seems desperately to be seeking some religious roots, some cosmic significance for mankind, may or may not be creditable. I think there is much good and much evil in the old-time religions. But I do not understand the need for half-measures. If we are forced to choose—and we *decidedly* are not—is the evidence not better for the God of Moses than for the comet of Velikovsky?

Acknowledgments

I am very grateful to many of my colleagues who have made helpful suggestions and criticisms, but particularly to Steven Soter, E. E. Salpeter, Thomas Gold, Philip Morrison, David Morrison, and Sidney Coleman.

Appendix 1. *Simple Collision Physics Discussion of the Probability of a Recent Collision with the Earth by a Massive Member of the Solar System*

We here consider, using the most elementary treatment which preserves the essential physics, the probability that a massive object of the sort considered by Velikovsky to be ejected from Jupiter might impact the Earth. Velikovsky proposes that a grazing or near collision occurred between this comet and the Earth. We will subsume this idea under the designation "collision" below. Consider a spherical object of radius R moving among other objects of similar size. Collision will occur when the centers of the objects are $2R$ distant. We may then speak of an effective collision cross section of $\sigma = \pi(2R)^2 = 4\pi R^2$; this is the target area which the center of the moving object must strike in order for a collision to occur. Let us assume that only one such object (Velikovsky's comet) is moving and that the others (the planets in the inner solar system) are stationary. This neglect of the motion of the planets of the inner solar system can be shown to introduce errors smaller than a factor of 2. Let the comet be moving at a velocity v and let the space density of potential targets (the planets of the inner solar system) be n. We will use units in which R is in centimeters (cm), σ is in cm^2, v is in cm/sec, and n is in planets per cm^3; n is obviously a very small number.

While comets have a wide range of orbital inclinations to the ecliptic plane, we will be making the most generous assumptions for Velikovsky's hypothesis if we assume the smallest plausible value for this inclination. If there were no restrictions on the orbital inclination of the comet, it would have equal likelihood of moving anywhere in a volume centered on the sun and of radius $r = 5$ astronomical units ($1 \text{ a.u.} = 1.5 \times 10^{13}$cm), the semi-major axis of the orbit of Jupiter. The larger the volume in which the comet can move, the less likely is any collision of it with another object. Because of Jupiter's rapid rotation, any object flung out from its interior will have a tendency to move in the planet's equatorial plane, which is inclined by 1.2° to the plane of the Earth's revolution about the sun. However, for the comet to reach the inner part of the solar system at all, the ejection event must be sufficiently energetic that virtually any value of its orbital inclination,i, is plausible. A generous lower limit is then $i = 1.2°$. We, therefore, consider the comet to move (Figure 2) in an orbit contained somewhere in a wedge-shaped volume, centered on the sun (the comet's orbit must have the sun at one focus), and of half-angle i. Its volume is then $(4/3)\pi r^3 \sin i = 4 \times 10^{40}$ cm^3, only 2 percent the full volume of a sphere of radius, r. Since in that volume there are (neglecting the asteroids) three or four planets, the space density of targets relevant for our problem is about 10^{-40} planets/cm^3. A typical relative velocity of a comet or other object moving on an eccentric orbit in the inner solar system might be about 20 km/sec. The radius of the Earth is $R = 6.3 \times 10^8$ cm, which is almost exactly the radius of the planet Venus as well.

Now let us imagine that the elliptical path of the comet is, in our mind's eye, straightened out, and that it travels for some time, T, until it impacts a planet. During that time, it will have carved out an imaginary tunnel behind it of volume $\sigma v T$ cm^3, and in that volume there must be just one planet. But $1/n$ is also the volume containing one planet. Therefore, the two quantities are equal and $T = (n\sigma v)^{-1}$; T is called the mean free time.

In reality, of course, the comet will be traveling on an elliptical orbit, and the time for collision will be influenced to some degree by gravitational forces. However, it is easy to show (see,

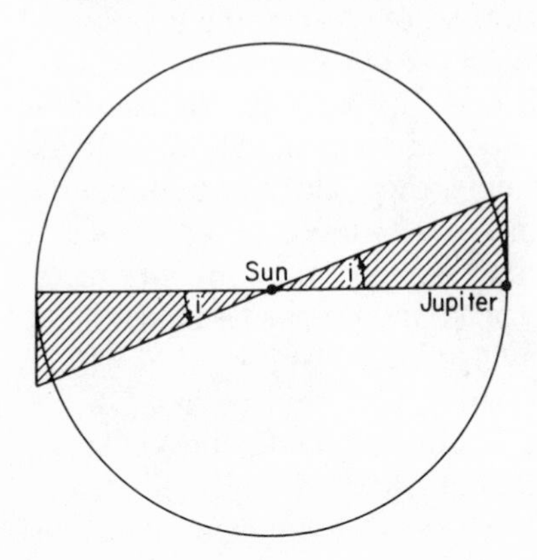

Figure 2. Wedge-shaped volume occupied by Velikovsky's comet

e.g., Urey, 1951) that, for typical values of v and relatively brief excursions of solar-system history such as Velikovsky is considering, the gravitational effects are to increase the effective collision cross section σ by a small quantity; and a rough calculation using the above equation must give approximately the right results.

The objects which have, since the earliest history of the solar system, produced impact craters on the moon, the Earth, and the inner planets are ones in highly eccentric orbits: the comets and, especially, the Apollo objects—which are either dead comets or asteroids. Using simple equations for the mean free time, astronomers are able to account to good accuracy for, say, the number of craters on the moon, Mercury, or Mars: the craters are the results of the occasional collision of an Apollo object or, more rarely, a comet with the lunar or planetary surface. Likewise, the equation predicts correctly the age of the most recent impact craters on the Earth such as Meteor Crater, Arizona. These quantitative agreements between observations and simple collision physics provide some substantial assurance that the same considerations properly apply to the present problem.

We are now able to make some calculations with regard to Velikovsky's fundamental hypothesis. At the present time, no Apollo objects exist with diameters larger than a few tens of kilometers. The sizes of objects in the asteroid belt, and indeed anywhere else where collisions determine sizes, are understood by comminution physics. The number of objects in a given size range is proportional to the radius of the object to some negative power, usually in the range of 2 to 4. If, therefore, Velikovsky's proto-Venus comet were a member of some family of objects like the Apollo objects or the comets, the chance of finding one Velikovskian comet 6,000 km in radius would be far less than one-millionth of the chance of finding one some tens of km in radius. A more probable number is a billion times less likely, but let us give the benefit of the doubt to Velikovsky.

Since there are approximately 10 Apollo objects larger than about 10 km in radius, the chance of there being one Velikovskian comet is then much less than a hundred thousand to one odds against the proposition. The steady-state abundance of such an object would then be (for $r = 4$ a.u., and $i = 1.2°$) $n = (10 \times 10^{-5})/4 \times 10^{40} = 2.5 \times 10^{-45}$ Velikovskian comets/cm^3. The mean free time for collision with the Earth would then be $T = 1/(n\sigma v) = 1/[(2.5 \times 10^{-45}\ \text{cm}^{-3}) \times (5 \times 10^{18}\ \text{cm}^2) \times (2 \times 10^6\ \text{cm sec}^{-1})] = 4 \times 10^{21}$ secs $\simeq 10^{14}$ years which is much greater than the age of the solar system (5×10^9 years). That is, if the Velikovskian comet were part of the population of other colliding debris in the inner solar system, it would be such a rare object that it would essentially never collide with the Earth. But instead let us grant Velikovsky's hypothesis for the sake of argument and ask how long his comet would require, after ejection from Jupiter, to collide with a planet in the inner solar system. Then, n applies to the abundance of planetary targets rather than Velikovskian comets, and $T = 1/[10^{-40}\ \text{cm}^{-3}) \times (5 \times 10^{18}\ \text{cm}^2) \times (2 \times 10^6\ \text{cm sec}^{-1})] = 10^{15}$ secs $\simeq 3 \times 10^7$ years. Thus, the chance of Velikovsky's comet making a single full or grazing collision with the Earth within the last few thousand years is $(3 \times 10^4)/(3 \times 10^7) = 10^{-3}$, or one chance in a thousand—if it is independent of the other debris populations. If it is part of such populations, the odds rise to $(3 \times 10^4)/10^{14} = 3 \times 10^{-10}$, or one chance in 3 billion.

A more exact formulation of orbital collision theory can be found in the classic paper by Ernst Öpik (1951). He considers a target body of mass m_o with orbital elements a_o, $e_o = i_o = 0$ in orbit about a central body of mass M. Then, a test body of mass m with orbital elements a, e, i and period P has a characteristic time T before approaching within distance R of the target body, where

$$\frac{T}{P} = \frac{\pi \sin i |U_x/U|}{Q^2[1 + 2(m_o + m)/MQU]},$$

$$A = a/a_o, \qquad Q = R/a_o,$$

$$|U_x| = [2 - \frac{1}{A} - A(1 - e^2)]^{\frac{1}{2}}$$

$$U = \{3 - \frac{1}{A} - 2\,[A(1 - e^2)]^{\frac{1}{2}} \cos i\}^{\frac{1}{2}};$$

here, U is the relative velocity "at infinity" and U_x is its component along the line of nodes.

If R is taken as the physical radius of the planet, then

	Venus	*Earth*	*Mars*	*Jupiter*
$Q \times 10^5$	5.6	4.3	1.5	8.8
$2m_0/MQ$	0.088	0.14	0.043	21.6

For application of Öpik's results to the present problem, the equations reduce to the following approximation:

$$\frac{T}{P} \simeq \frac{\pi \sin i}{Q^2}$$

Using $P \simeq 5$ years ($a \simeq 3$ a.u.), we have $T \simeq 9 \times 10^9 \sin i$ years, or about one-third the mean free path lifetime from the simpler argument above.

Note that in both calculations, an approach to within N Earth radii has N^2 times the probability of a physical collision. Thus, for $N = 10$, a miss of 63,000 km, the above values of T must be reduced by two orders of magnitude. This is about one-sixth the distance between the Earth and the moon. For the Velikovskian scenario to apply, a closer approach is necessary: the book, after all, is called *Worlds in Collision*. Also, it is claimed (page 87) that, as a result of the passage of Venus by the Earth, the oceans were piled to a height of sixteen hundred miles. From this it is easy to calculate backwards from simple tidal theory (the tide height is proportional to M/r^3, where M is the mass of Venus and r the distance between the planets during the encounter) that Velikovsky is talking about a grazing collision: the surfaces of Earth and Venus scrape! But note that even a 63,000-km miss does not extricate the hypothesis from the collision-physics problems as outlined in this Appendix.

Finally, we observe that an orbit which intersects those of Jupiter and Earth implies a high probability of a close reapproach to Jupiter which would eject the object from the solar system before a near encounter with the Earth—a natural example of the trajectory of the Pioneer 10 spacecraft. Therefore, the present existence of the planet Venus must imply that the Velikovskian comet made few subsequent passages to Jupiter, and therefore that its orbit was circularized rapidly. (That there seems to be no way to accomplish such rapid circularization is discussed in the text.) Accordingly, Velikovsky must suppose that the comet's close encounter with the Earth occurred soon after its ejection from Jupiter—which is consistent with the above calculations.

The probability, then, that the comet would have impacted the Earth only some tens of years after its ejection from Jupiter is between one chance in a million and one chance in 3 trillion, on the two assumptions on membership in existing debris populations. Even if we were to suppose that the comet was ejected from Jupiter as Velikovsky says, and make the unlikely assumption that it has no relation to any other objects which we see in the solar system today—that is, that smaller objects are never ejected from Jupiter—the mean waiting time for it to have impacted the Earth would be about 30,000,000 years—which is inconsistent with this hypothesis by a factor of about one million. When we include the fact that Velikovsky believes in several statistically independent collisions in a few hundred years (see text), the net likelihood that his hypothesis is true becomes vanishing small. His repeated planetary encounters would require what might be called "Worlds in Collusion."

Appendix 2. *Consequences of a Sudden Deceleration of the Earth's Rotation*

Q. Now, Mr. Bryan, have you ever pondered what would have happened to the Earth if it had stood still?
A. No. The God I believe in could have taken care of that, Mr. Darrow.
Q. Don't you know that it would have been converted into a molten mass of matter?
A. You testify to that when you get on the stand. I will give you a chance.

—The Scopes Trial, 1925

The gravitational acceleration which holds us to the Earth's surface has a value of 10^3 cm $sec^{-2} = 1$ g. A deceleration of

$a = 10^{-2}$ g $= 10$ cm sec^{-2} is almost unnoticeable. How much time, τ, would the Earth take to stop its rotation if the resulting deceleration were unnoticeable? The Earth's equatorial angular velocity is $\Omega = 2\pi/P = 7.3 \times 10^{-5}$ radians/sec; the equatorial linear velocity is $R\Omega = 0.46$ km/sec. Thus, $\tau = R\Omega/a = 4600$ secs, or a little over an hour.

The specific energy of the Earth's rotation is $E = \frac{1}{2}I\Omega^2/M \simeq 1/5\ (R\Omega)^2 \simeq 4 \times 10^8$ erg gm^{-1}, where I is the Earth's principal moment of inertia. This is less than the latent heat of fusion for silicates, $L \simeq 4 \times 10^9$ erg gm^{-1}. Thus, Clarence Darrow was wrong about the Earth's melting. Nevertheless, he was on the right track: thermal considerations are in fact fatal to the Joshua story. With a typical specific heat capacity of $c_p \simeq 8 \times 10^6$ erg gm^{-1} deg^{-1}, the stopping and restarting of the Earth in one day would have imparted an *average* temperature increment of $\Delta T \simeq 2E/c_p \simeq 100°$K, enough to raise the temperature above the normal boiling point of water. It would have been even worse near the surface and at low latitudes; with $v \simeq R\Omega$, $\Delta T \simeq v^2/c_p \simeq 240°$K. It is doubtful that the inhabitants would have failed to notice so dramatic a climatic change. The deceleration might be tolerable, if gradual enough, but not the heat.

Appendix 3. *Present Temperature of Venus If Heated by a Close Passage to the Sun*

The heating of Venus by a presumed close passage by the sun, and the planet's subsequent cooling by radiation to space are central to the Velikovskian thesis. But nowhere does he calculate either the amount of heating or the rate of cooling. However, at least a crude calculation can be performed readily. An object which grazes the solar photosphere must travel at very high velocities if it originates in the outer solar system: 500 km/sec is a typical value at perihelion passage. But the radius of the sun is 7×10^{10} cm. Therefore a typical time scale for the heating of Velikovsky's comet is $(1.4 \times 10^{11}$ cm$) / (5 \times 10^7$ cm/sec$) \simeq 3000$ secs, which is less than an hour. The highest temperature the comet could possibly reach because of its close approach to the sun is 6,000°K, the temperature of the solar photosphere. Velikovsky does not discuss any further sun-grazing events by his comet; subsequently, it becomes the planet Venus, and cools by radiating to space—events which occupy, say, thirty-five hundred years up to the present. But both heating and cooling occur radiatively, and the physics of both events is controlled in the same way by the Stefan-Boltzmann law of thermodynamics, according to which the amount of heating and the rate of cooling both are proportional to the temperature to the fourth power. Therefore, the ratio of the temperature increment experienced by the comet in 3,000 secs of solar heating to its temperature decrement in thirty-five hundred years of radiative cooling is $(3 \times 10^3 \text{ secs}/10^{11} \text{ secs})^{1/4} = 0.013$. The present temperature of Venus from this source would then be at most only $6{,}000 \times 0.013 = 79$°K or about the temperature at which air freezes. Velikovsky's mechanism cannot keep Venus hot, even with very generous definitions of the word "hot."

The conclusion would not be materially altered were there to have been several close passes, rather than just one, through the solar photosphere. The source of the high temperature of Venus cannot be one or a few heating events, no matter how dramatic. The hot surface requires a continuous source of heat—which could be either endogenous (radioactive heating from the planetary interior) or exogenous (sunlight). It is now evident, as suggested many years ago (Wildt, 1940; Sagan, 1960), that the latter is the case: it is the present radiation of the sun, continuously falling on Venus, which is responsible for its high surface temperature.

Appendix 4. *Magnetic Field Strengths Necessary to Circularize an Eccentric Cometary Orbit*

Although Velikovsky has not made the calculation, we can approximate the order of magnitude of the magnetic field strength necessary to make a significant perturbation on the motion of a comet. The perturbing field might be from a planet, such as the Earth or Mars, to which the comet is about to make a close approach, or from the interplanetary magnetic field. For this field to play an important role, its energy density must be comparable to the kinetic energy density of the comet. (We do not even worry about whether the comet has a distribution of charges and fields which will permit it to respond to the imposed field.) Thus, the condition is

$$\frac{B^2}{8\pi} = \frac{\frac{1}{2}mv^2}{(4/3)\pi R^3} = \frac{1}{2}\rho v^2$$

where B is the magnetic field strength in gauss, R is the radius of the comet, m its mass, v its velocity and ρ its density. We note that the condition is independent of the mass of the comet. Taking a typical cometary velocity in the inner solar system of about 25 km/sec, and ρ as the density of Venus, about 5 gm/cm^3, we find that a magnetic field strength of over 10 million gauss is required. (A similar value in electrostatic units would apply if the circularization is electrical rather than magnetic.) The Earth's equatorial surface field is about 0.5 gauss. The fields of Mars and Venus are less than 0.01 gauss. The sun's field is several gauss, ranging up to several hundred gauss in sunspots. Jupiter's field as measured by Pioneer 10 is less than 10 gauss. Typical interplanetary fields are 10^{-5} gauss. There is no way to generate anything approaching a 10 megagauss field on a large scale in the solar system. And there is no sign that such a field was ever experienced in the vicinity of the Earth. We recall that the magnetic domains of molten rock in the course of refreezing are oriented by the prevailing field. Had the Earth experienced, even fairly briefly, a 10 megagauss field thirty-five hundred years ago, rock magnetization evidence would show it clearly. It does not.

References

Brandt, J. C., S. P. Maran, and T. P. Stecher. "Astronomers Ask Archaeologists' Aid," *Archaeology* 21:360, 1971.

Brandt, J. C., S. P. Maran, R. Williamson, R. Harrington, C. Cochran, M. Kennedy, W. Kennedy, and V. Chamberlain. "Possible Rock Art Records of the

Crab Nebula Supernova in the Western United States," in A. F. Aveni, ed., *Archaeoastronomy in Pre-Columbian America* (Austin: University of Texas Press, 1974).

Brown, Harrison. "Rare Gases and the Formation of the Earth's Atmosphere," in Gerard Kuiper, ed., *The Atmospheres of the Earth and Planets* (Chicago: University of Chicago Press, 1949).

Campbell, J. *The Mythic Image* (Princeton: Princeton University Press, 1974; 2d pr., with corrections, 1975).

Connes, P., J. Connes, W. S. Benedict, and L. D. Kaplan. "Traces of HC*l* and HF in the Atmosphere of Venus," *Ap. J.* 147:1230, 1967.

Covey, C. *Anthropological Journal of Canada* 13:2–10, 1975.

de Camp, L. Spragne. *Lost Continents: The Atlantis Theme* (New York: Ballantine Books, 1975).

Dodd, Edward. *Polynesian Seafaring* (New York: Dodd Mead, 1972).

Ehrlich, Max. *The Big Eye* (New York: Doubleday, 1949).

Galanopoulos, Angelos G. "Die Ägyptischen Plagen und der Auszug Israels aus Geologischer Sicht," *Das Altertum* 10:131–137, 1964.

Gould, S. J. "Velikovsky in Collision," *Natural History* 3:20–26, 1975.

Kuiper, Gerard P., ed. *The Atmospheres of the Earth and Planets* (Chicago: University of Chicago Press, 1949).

Leach, E. R. "Primitive Time Reckoning," in C. Singer, E. J. Holmyard, and A. R. Hall, eds., *The History of Technology* (London: Oxford University Press, 1954).

Lecar, Myron, and Fred A. Franklin. "On the Original Distribution of the Asteroids," *Icarus* 20:422–436, 1973.

Marov, M. Ya. "Venus: A Perspective at the Beginning of Planetary Exploration," *Icarus* 16:415–461, 1972.

Marov, M. Ya., V. Avduevsky, N. Borodin, A. Ekonomov, V. Kerzhanovich, V. Lysov, B. Moshkin, M. Rozhdestvensky, and O. Ryabov. "Preliminary Results on the Venus Atmosphere from the Venera 8 Descent Module," *Icarus* 20:407–421, 1973.

Meeus, J. "Comments on *The Jupiter Effect*," *Icarus* 26:257–267, 1975.

Neugebauer, O. "Ancient Mathematics and Astronomy," in C. Singer, E. J. Holmyard, and A. R. Hall, eds., *The History of Technology* (London: Oxford University Press, 1954).

Öpik, Ernst J. "Collision Probabilities with the Planets and the Distribution of Interplanetary Matter," *Proceedings of the Royal Irish Academy* 54:165–199, 1951.

Owen, T. C., and C. Sagan. "Minor Constitutents in Planetary Atmospheres: Ultraviolet Spectroscopy from the Orbiting Astronomical Observatory," *Icarus* 16:557–568, 1972.

Pollack, J. B. "A Nongray CO_2-H_2O Greenhouse Model of Venus, *Icarus* 10:314–341, 1969.

Pollack, J. B., E. Erickson, F. Witteborn, C. Chackerian, A. Summers, G. Augason, and L. Caroff. "Aircraft Observation of Venus' Near-infrared Reflection Spectrum: Implications for Cloud Composition," *Icarus* 23:8–26, 1974.

Sagan, Carl. "The Radiation Balance of Venus," California Institute of Technology, Jet Propulsion Laboratory, Technical Report 32–34 (1960).

——. "The Planet Venus," *Science* 133:849, 1961.

——. *The Cosmic Connection* (New York: Doubleday, 1973).
——. "Erosion of the Rocks of Venus," *Nature* 261:31, 1976.
Sagan, C. and T. Page, eds., *UFO's: A Scientific Debate* (Ithaca, N.Y.: Cornell University Press, 1972; New York: Norton, 1973).
Sill, G. "Sulfuric Acid in the Venus Clouds," Communications Lunar Planet Lab., University of Arizona, 9:191–198, 1972.
Spitzer, Lyman, and Walter Baade. "Stellar Populations and Collisions of Galaxies," *Ap. J.* 113:413, 1951.
Urey, Harold C. *The Planets* (New Haven: Yale University Press, 1951).
——. "Cometary Collisions and Geological Periods," *Nature* 242:32–33, 1973.
Velikovsky, I. *Worlds in Collision* (New York: Doubleday, 1950; reprinted, Dell, 1965).
——. "Venus, a Youthful Planet," *Yale Scientific Magazine* 41:8–11, 1967.
Vitaliano, Dorothy B. *Legends of the Earth: Their Geologic Origins* (Bloomington, Ind.: Indiana University Press, 1973).
Wheelock, J. "Mariner: Mission to Venus" (Pasadena, Calif.: Jet Propulsion Laboratory, 1963).
Wildt, Rupert. "On the Chemistry of the Atmosphere of Venus," *Ap. J.* 96:312–314, 1942.
——. "Note on the Surface Temperature of Venus," *Ap. J.* 91:266, 1940.
Young, A. T. "Are the Clouds of Venus Sulfuric Acid?" *Icarus* 18:564–582, 1973.
Young, L. D. G., and A. T. Young. "The Composition of the Venus Cloud Tops in Light of Recent Spectroscopic Data," *Ap. J.* 179:L39, 1973.

3 Movements of Celestial Bodies—Velikovsky's Fatal Flaw

J. DERRAL MULHOLLAND

Within the folk memory of man, Venus and Mars erupted into the sky and rushed close by Earth and each other several times, creating unimaginable destruction. The Earth stopped turning, the poles shifted, the year and month changed. Civilizations were destroyed. Finally, the two giant comets settled down into their present harmless orbits and became peaceable planets, leaving behind a legacy of fear codified into religious belief. Only the healing passage of time erased the memory of these events from the collective consciousness of mankind. This is the vision presented to us by Immanuel Velikovsky to explain the foundations of religion and folk myth. Could it have happened? Did it happen? How can we tell?

If it is the function of science to explain man's relation to his universe, then these are questions of serious significance and should be dealt with seriously. Velikovsky's challenge is not one to be decided on a basis of belief or unbelief. He does not say, "Trust me"; he says, "This conclusion is suggested by the observations." He strives, it seems to me, to build physically plausible solutions that involve testable ideas. He is not a mystic. He doesn't use little green men with three ears; he uses real planets. It is not sufficient to reply that his ideas are absurd: there are too many examples of absurd ideas come true.

Are the explanations plausible? From at least one vantage point, yes indeed. *If* a planet-sized object were to pass close by the Earth, then giant tides would be raised; there would be global earthquakes; the north pole would change direction; the day, the month, the seasons, the year would all change. Faith is not involved here; these are unavoidable consequences of the laws of motion as we presently know them. We must accept that the dynamical aspects of Velikovsky's visions of hell on Earth are largely acceptable. This is not to admit that the events he described ever happened, for there remain three questions that need to be resolved. Does our knowledge of the laws of motion permit or deny the possibility of encounters between the known planets? Are Velikovsky's interpretations of certain information the best available ones? Are there uncited observational data that confirm or refute the hypothesis of repeated cosmic catastrophe? We must try to answer these questions on the basis of the reality of causes and the record of events. We must guard against appeals to faith, in support either of orthodoxy or of novelty. If we adhere to these principles, then dynamics offers perhaps the most clear-cut contradiction to the evil influences of Venus and Mars.

But today the celestial mechanics of Sir Isaac Newton and Simon Newcomb are no longer the ultimate measure. Today, celestial mechanics is a living, vital science that admits of nongravitational effects, of electromagnetic interactions, of flexible astral bodies, and of statistical descriptions of some types of occurrences involving large numbers of bodies. In spite of our new knowledge, however, some unrecognized influences may yet remain.

Did the Axis Tilt?

A major feature of Velikovsky's theory is that the Earth was suddenly disturbed in its rotation: the axis of rotation shifted relative to the stars, and the crust of the Earth shifted relative to the rotational pole; perhaps the rotation itself stopped or temporarily reversed. The evidence consists of mythical accounts of the sun standing still, prolonging day or night, of the strange depiction of the southern sky in an Egyptian tomb, and of discrepancies in ancient and modern determinations of the latitude of certain sites.

The occurrence of supernaturally long days and nights pervades folklore all over the globe, and Velikovsky's recitation of numerous passages is very impressive, but perhaps sufficiently repetitive to deaden one's skepticism. That the length of time consumed by these events varies from three to ten days is dismissed as due to the inability of the story teller to determine time accurately. Indeed, we are also told[1] that the difference between seven and nine days is negligible among a people who are elsewhere[2] said to have clocks of high accuracy. Perhaps more damaging to his case is his report on the geographic distribution of day and night, which appears to contain some geometric inconsistencies. No matter where the poles lie, no matter what the orientation of the globe, light and dark must each occupy a complete hemisphere. The myths do not seem to satisfy this simple requirement.

The objectionable feature of the chart in the tomb of Senmut seems to be that it shows the southern sky as seen from the Southern Hemisphere. It is not necessary to suppose (as Velikovsky does) that this indicates the hemispheres have been physically reversed in space. Indeed, this switch would require either that the description of the *northern* sky be anomalous or that the murals represent different epochs. It is enough to know[3] that the Egyptians had already made sea voyages around the Cape of Good Hope and had seen the southern sky pivoting about the other pole.

Velikovsky's discussion of latitudes suffers two assumptions, either of which may be doubted: first, that observations and clocks were completely accurate twenty-seven centuries ago, and second, that they were made and used at the sites where they were found. On this basis, Velikovsky's statement implies[4] that Babylon has moved southward by some 250 kilometers. Further, Velikovsky gives no estimate for the distance covered in his shift in location of Faijum in Egypt, but states that the sundial found at Faijum does not read true there or at any other place in Egypt.[5] While he does not say that it would read true anywhere else, we can understand that it would only be at a higher latitude. Indeed, Velikovsky implies that Faijum has shifted southward. Finally, the water clock at Thebes is cited,[6] with the emphasis on the clock error rather than on what the error implies. This seems quite understandable, since Velikovsky's interpretation of the clock error requires Thebes to have moved 1,000 kilometers northward while the other Near-Eastern cities moved southward. It is difficult to reconcile these requirements.

Do places change their latitude? Yes, certainly. Changes have been observed amounting to a few meters per year. Have latitudes changed by tens of degrees, thousands of kilometers? Almost certainly, if one uses geologic time scales. Does Velikovsky's evidence provide reasonable proof that the axis shifted abruptly and catastrophically twenty-seven centuries ago? Absolutely not.

The Day, the Month, and the Year

Until recently, time could only be reckoned in terms of celestial motions. The day is governed by the rotation of Earth on its axis, the month by the revolution of the moon in its Earth-centered orbit, and the year by the revolution of Earth in its sun-centered orbit. Various kinds of clocks have been devised to subdivide the day, but only the atomic clock invented in 1955 is truly independent and accurate. How then does one determine the history of the length of the day, how to know if the rotation has been changed? The brute fact is that we cannot do so entirely unambiguously for the years before 1955; thus, one must adopt some guiding principle from which to evaluate the evidence we have available. Velikovsky's principle is that stories surviving from a time of primitive technology can be accepted as evidence of highly reliable observations with accurate instruments of known location. This seems bizarre when more reasonable principles exist: one could examine the solar system for clues to the past. But Velikovsky is correct in rejecting the supposed stability of the solar system as a valid counterargument. This stability has not been proved and would only constitute a valid concept so long as no large exterior bodies entered the system. One cannot say that this will not happen, or even that it has not happened. On the other hand, there is evidence that the size of Earth's orbit has not changed much in the recent past. It has long been noted that there is a remarkably regular pattern in the spacing of most of the planet orbits (this was a subject of concern to Kepler). The near-circularity of the orbits is not easily obtained and is most readily explained as the result either of the formation process or of the gradual action of friction (it would be very difficult to produce circular orbits by a small number of near collisions, as Velikovsky proposes). Admittedly, one cannot rule out a year that differs by 1 or 2 percent from 365 days, but a year of 300 modern days would increase solar heating by 20 percent. Such a significant change would probably be fatal to *all* higher life forms. If this is so, then major changes in the number of days per year may be interpreted as changes in the length of the day. Similarly, major changes in the number of months per year indicate changes in the lunar orbit.

We know that slow changes are occurring now in the length of the day and the month, as measured with atomic clocks; no such change, however, has yet been found for the year. The current measurements show that the length of the day is increasing by about 2 milliseconds per century.[7] A study of ancient astronomical records from −763 onwards (we shall use plus and minus signs to denote dates A.D. and B.C.)[8] yields an average increase over a period of two thousand years of 2.4 milliseconds, with indications that small abrupt changes occurred around the years +700 and +1300, but not earlier. Another study,[9] using observations dating back to −1300 gives results that are not compatible with large abrupt changes in the pre-Christian era. Various studies of growth rings in fossil materials,[10] which show an average increase of 2 milliseconds over the past 360 million years (with the average somewhat higher over the past 70 million), thus provide us with a physical record that indicates a pattern of reasonable continuity in the length of the day. Astronomical data spanning the years in which at least some of Velikovsky's catastrophes occurred show no disruption. Either the events did not happen, or multiple events served to offset each other, leaving no astronomical record of the events. But friction would produce a large part of the total effect in a rotation change, and friction is not reversible.

The same observations, or many of them, apply to the length of the month. Eclipses involve the moon, and tidal cycles affect growth rings. But there are no evidences of cataclysmic changes in the number of months per year. Was there ever a 30-day month? Yes, about 60 million years ago, when the year had 380 days.[11] Was there ever a 10-month year? No, not earlier than ten million years ago or more recently than thirty-three hundred years ago. Could there have been between those dates? Not unless multiple events canceled each other in their effects on *both* the lunar orbit and the Earth rotation, returning them to the smooth sequence of the observations. These events would also be required to leave the moon in a near-circular orbit near the plane of the ecliptic. It requires a great act of faith to believe this.

Further evidence comes from the spin rates of other objects in the solar system as well. At first sight, these rotations are a bit chaotic, but in fact they are remarkably regular. There is a smooth sequence of angular momentum as a function of mass which is satisfied by nearly all of the planets, as well as by all of the asteroids whose spins are known.[12] This relationship, which covers five orders of magnitude in mass, can only be related to the formation of the entire system and is evidence for a long interval of stability.[13] The objects that do not conform are, with one exception, those that are known to have been slowed by tidal friction. The spin of Mercury has been captured by the sun, while that of Venus has been captured by Earth. This latter, far from being evidence of a near collision, is in fact evidence against it, because the present spin of Venus is linked with the present orbits of the two bodies by tidal friction, a system which has been operating since those orbits were established. We *do* know something about the magnitude of the tides and the time required for them to be effective. Three millennia is far too short a time. The same argument applies for the rotation of the moon.[14]

It must be admitted that the rotation of Mars is a small embarrassment here, because in angular momentum it departs slightly from the general uniformity and apparently does not belong to the class of tidally influenced bodies. Still, there is no dynamical basis for Velikovsky's conjecture that its 24-hour period is due to a close encounter with Earth. One body influences another's spin rate through its overall force field, which is not much related to its own spin rate. The evidence from rotation periods may be summarized as follows: the rotation of Mars does not support Velikovsky; the rotations of Earth, Venus, moon, and nearly all other objects in the solar system refute the theory of recent catastrophe.

The Satellites of Earth and Mars

In addition to his conclusions about the lunar orbit, Velikovsky claims[15] that the huge lunar craters are the remnants of burst bubbles that welled up when the near collisions melted the lunar surface. Ignoring the fact that rock does not cool fast enough to freeze such rings, the very existence of 100-kilometer bubbles requires that the moon be molten to a very great depth. The present shape of the moon, however, is strong evidence that it was never molten. No combination of orbit and spin could produce that shape.[16] Indeed, if there were general melting as recently as three thousand years ago, the surface would still be somewhat plastic, proof of which is refuted by the existence of mascons, as well as by the Apollo mission rock studies.

It is also claimed that Jonathan Swift's description of Mars' satellites prior to their discovery is evidence that the ancients had seen them when that planet passed close by the Earth. Based on the knowledge and philosophy available at the time, Swift's guess is not really so remarkable as Velikovsky believes. Far from supporting his case, the existence of these two tiny rocks in near-circular orbits near the plane of gravitational symmetry are the most positive proof that Mars has *not* had a near collision with Earth, Venus, or any other major body for an astronomically long period. In any such encounter, the satellites would have been severely disturbed, if not stripped away from Mars entirely.[17]

Where Do Comets Come From?

The catastrophic hypothesis supposes that comets, including Venus, erupted from Jupiter just prior to the encounters with Earth. The justifications for this history are the myths concerning the birth of the Venus goddess, the fact that many comets are observed to have Jupiter-related orbits, and the belief that comets were more numerous in ancient times than now. Of course, dynamics cannot be used to comment upon folk tales, or vice versa. Further, I do not believe that the third point is well founded. Frequently, no distinction seems to have been made in ancient times between comets and meteors. Both were considered to be atmospheric phenomena. The orbital association with Jupiter is real, however, and must be dealt with.

There does not seem to be any fundamental difference between long-period comets (i.e., those whose orbits extend to the outer reaches of the solar system) and short-period comets, which suggests that they all have a common, or at least a similar, origin. No comet has ever been seen to erupt from Jupiter in modern times, but Comet Kohoutek recently passed through on an orbit with a period in excess of 100,000 years.[18] No short-period comet has been seen to be ejected from the solar system, and indeed numerical experiments show that it is much more difficult to eject short-period comets than it is to capture long-period comets into smaller orbits. The main agent in such captures would be Jupiter, by far the most massive planet. The observed number of long-period comets, together with capture dynamics, is quite adequate to explain the observed number of short-period comets.[19] The number of long-period comets is consistent with the existence of a comet belt (rather like the asteroid belt) in the far reaches of the system. If such a belt exists, occasional encounters would inevitably inject comets into hairpin trajectories toward the sun where the planets would try their best to capture them—as if engaged in some great celestial billiard game. As Velikovsky notes, Jupiter has been observed to modify comet orbits, but there is no support for his main hypotheses in this observed dynamical behavior of comets.

Collisions and Near Misses

What are our space warriors doing today? Really, the orbital paths of Venus, Earth, and Mars are remarkably ordinary. All are near the same plane, and all are slightly elliptical rather than circular.[20] Venus passes within 30 million miles of Earth, while Mars rarely gets as close as 40 million miles. Yet, according to Velikovsky, we are to imagine them on elongated paths, making repeated strafing runs on Earth, until some force caused them to settle down and leave the world at peace. Today, we know a great deal about orbital transfer mechanics, the process of changing an object's path in the sky. We know not only the effects of gravity, but also the effects of electric and magnetic forces acting on an orbit, the drag exerted by atmospheres, the push of internal explosions and escaping gas. The Mariner 9 spacecraft was in fact transferred from an elongated Earth-crossing orbit into the orbit of Mars by a conscious application of this knowledge. While our understanding of celestial mechanics may not be complete, still both theoretical and experimental knowledge exists of each of the factors that Velikovsky supposes to have influenced the motions. To put Venus and Mars into their present orbits would have required the application of outside forces thousands of times more powerful than those needed to tilt the Earth's axis, disturb the rotation, and destroy the landscape. There is no agent available to provide those outside forces. One could hypothesize two additional planet-sized objects entering the solar system, one encountering Venus, the other Mars, in just such a way as to produce near-circular orbits, then exiting the system without another trace. Or one could appeal to a host of angels pushing in just the right direction. Neither is believable.

The present-day orbits of Venus and Mars are ordinary but not totally undistinguished. Both have features that give evidence of a long interval of relative stability. The orbit of Venus exhibits a weak resonance with that of Earth. There are similar resonances between the orbit of Mars and those of numerous asteroids.[21] These features can best be interpreted as dynamical vestiges of the process by which the inner solar system was originally formed. These observed motions are not compatible with recently changed orbits.

It is not possible to say that encounters between celestial objects do not happen. Various impact craters on Earth, moon, and Mars attest to their occurrence. It is probable, though not certain, that the moon and several satellites of other planets were captured in near-miss encounters. Even Pluto was probably captured temporarily by Neptune and then lost again; although their orbits intersect, they will never collide, due to a strange gravitational waltz that keeps them separate.[22] The Earth has had near misses (astronomically speaking) with a whole family of asteroids, as well as with Comet Halley in 1910 (the true comet of the century). Indeed, each year, the Earth collides with several meteor streams that are certainly the debris of dead comets. The possibility of such events is not in question. From a dynamical point of view, only two questions count. Our knowledge of the factors, gravitational and otherwise, that influence bodies in motion *absolutely denies* that either Venus or Mars can have had Earth-crossing orbits within astronomically recent time. The available observational data suggest strongly that *no* planet-sized object has passed near Earth in historic time, and probably not for a much longer time. I sympathize with Velikovsky's attempts to resolve geological and cultural paradoxes, but their solution is not to be found in wars of the worlds.

Notes

1. *Worlds in Collision* (New York: Doubleday, 1950), p. 59.
2. *Ibid.*, p. 323.
3. P. Herrmann, *Conquest By Man* (New York: Harper, 1954).
4. *Worlds in Collision*, pp. 315–316.
5. *Ibid.*, p. 321.
6. *Ibid.*, pp. 323–324.
7. L. V. Morrison, paper presented to Commission 31, International Astronomical Union, Sydney, Australia, 1973.
8. R. R. Newton, "Astronomical Evidence Concerning Non-Gravitational Forces in the Earth-Moon System," *Astrophysics and Space Science* 16:179, 197.

9. P. M. Muller, paper presented at colloquium on Lunar Dynamics and Observable Coordinate Systems, Houston, Texas, 1973.

10. G. Pannella, "Paleontological Evidence on the Earth's Rotational History since Early Precambrian," *Astrophysics and Space Science* 16:212, 1972.

11. Frequently, Velikovsky's calendar discussions falsely imply that a solar event, such as an equinox, should fall on the same day in a given lunar month each year.

12. F. F. Fish, Jr., "Angular Momenta of the Planets," *Icarus* 7:251, 1967.

13. This relation is also strong evidence against the hypothesis that the asteroids are remnants of a destroyed planet.

14. Velikovsky is quite wrong (*Earth in Upheaval* [New York: Doubleday, 1955], p. 277) when he claims that the lunar wobble is unexplained and possibly related to Earth's magnetic field.

15. *Worlds in Collision,* pp. 360–361.

16. Z. Kopal, "Moments of Inertia of the Lunar Globe, and their Bearing On Chemical Differentiation of its Outer Layers," *The Moon* 4:28, 1972.

17. Velikovsky is not only wrong, but also unkind, when he alleges (*Worlds in Collision,* p. 280) that Asaph Hall was ignorant of the appropriateness of his names for these rocks. His usage was quite deliberate.

18. *Sky and Telescope* 46:285, 1973.

19. A. H. Delsemme, "Origin of the Short Period Comets," *Astronomy and Astrophysics* 29:377, 1973.

20. Their ellipticities are about 1, 2 and 9%. For comparison, the average for the eight innermost planets is 6%. Pluto is omitted because its orbit is known to be controlled by Neptune.

21. S. F. Dermott and A. P. Lenham, "Stability of the Solar System: Evidence from the Asteroids," *The Moon* 5:294, 1972.

22. C. J. Cohen and E. C. Hubbard, "Libration of the Close Approaches of Pluto and Neptune," *Astronomical Journal* 70:10, 1965.

4 Early Cuneiform Evidence for the Existence of the Planet Venus

PETER J. HUBER

According to Immanuel Velikovsky,[1] Venus sprang forth from the planet Jupiter somewhat before the middle of the second millennium B.C., wandered erratically through space for several centuries, and settled into its present orbit only in the eighth century B.C.

Velikovsky draws on historical and archaeological evidence to support his hypothesis, but unfortunately his arguments are mainly based on late and secondary sources, in part on obsolete and erroneous translations, and therefore lack force. Moreover, he sometimes makes a complete muddle of texts, insights, periods, and places (for example, he assigns[2] Kugler's famous text SH 272—lunar calculations for the years 104 B.C. to 101 B.C., provenance Babylon—to the seventh century B.C. and to Nineveh, and uses this text to support his interpretation of events alleged to have taken place between 748 B.C. and 688 B.C.).

Admittedly, Velikovsky's conclusions may contain some truth, even if his arguments are incorrect. But the primary and early cuneiform sources from the second and third millennia B.C. do not support his contentions. On the contrary, they flatly contradict them.

Specifically, I shall present evidence for the following assertions:

(1) That Venus was known as the morning and evening star certainly by 1900 B.C., and that in archaic texts, shortly after

3000 B.C., it is mentioned as a star in connection with the rising and setting sun. Hence it was already in an orbit between the sun and the Earth.

(2) That according to sixteenth-century records (that is −1580 to −1560; we shall use the minus sign to denote dates B.C.), the observed motion of Venus at that time agrees satisfactorily with its motion as calculated from the currently accepted orbital elements—which shows that Venus' orbit in the sixteenth century B.C. was almost, if not completely, identical with the planet's orbit today. The same is true with regard to its brightness.

Background Information

Cuneiform writing was invented around −3000; the latest known text is dated +74 (74 A.D.); see Figure 1. Babylonian astronomy developed rather late: to the best of our knowledge, continuous astronomical observations started around −750, and mathematical astronomy began after −500. Little is known about the more primitive Babylonian astronomy of the second millennium B.C. Apart from the famous Venus observations in the time of Ammizaduga (sixteenth century B.C.; see below) and some other supposedly old astrological omina (series of predictions), there exist only a few texts (from −1100 or earlier) which list constellations that rise or set with the sun in a given month, and there are some speculations about the size of the universe, but that is about all.

We can glean some additional information about the older times from mythological and religious texts that take us back to the time shortly after −2000 when Sumerian was dying out as a spoken language in Babylon and was superseded by Akkadian. Most Sumerian myths are preserved on tablets from that time, but they represent a much older oral tradition.

The most eminent goddess of the Sumerian pantheon is Inanna (a Sumerian word meaning Queen of Heaven), a goddess who was later identified with the Semitic Ishtar. In her three principal aspects she is the goddess of love, of war, and of the planet Venus.[3]

Figure 1. Babylonian chronology

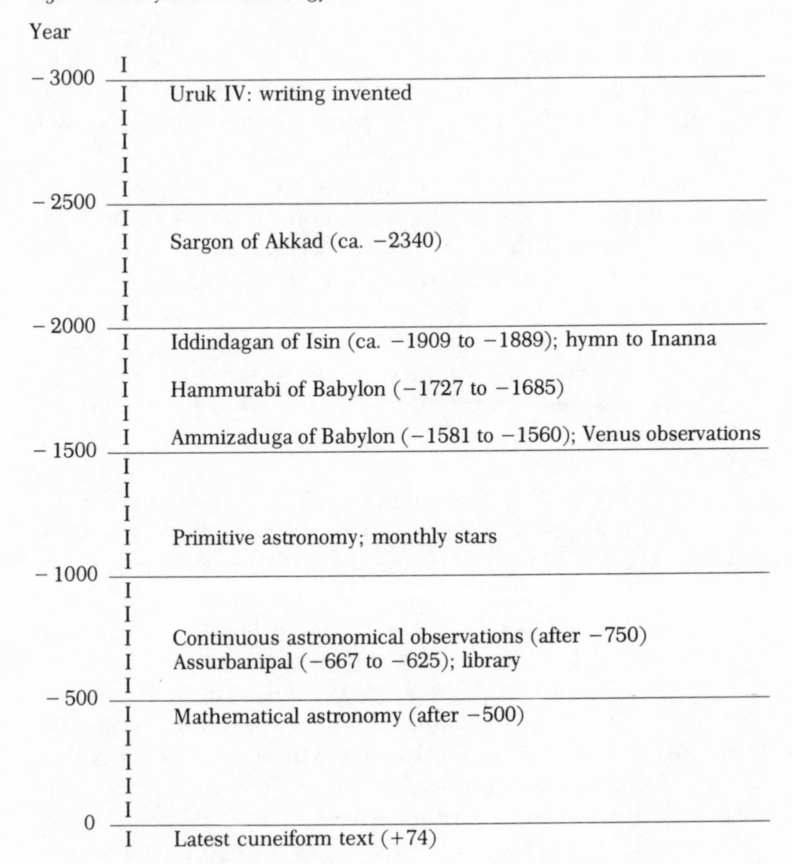

Pre-Old-Babylonian Evidence for the Planet Venus

There are many explicit and oblique early literary references to the astral character of Inanna. For instance, in the Sumerian version of "Inanna's descent to the nether world," which is preserved in copies from the early second millennium B.C., Inanna identifies herself to the gatekeeper of the nether world with the words, "I am Inanna of the place where the sun rises" (that is, the morning star).[4]

The most explicit and earliest of these literary references is contained in a beautiful hymn to Inanna as the goddess of the planet Venus. It is datable by the fact that it casts King Iddin-dagan of Isin (ca. −1909 to −1889) in the role of her mate Dumuzi. The text belongs to the sacred marriage rites, in which the king and a priestess substitute for the divine couple. In this text, the astral character of Inanna emerges clearly ("when she, like sun or moon, steps to the sky"), and the text even exhibits clearly and repeatedly Inanna's dual manifestation as the evening star ("in the evening she is the strange star, the Venus star") and as the morning star ("the strange[5] star, the Venus star, the queen of the morning").[6] Thus, Venus must have been in an orbit between the sun and the Earth around −1900, for only those planets with orbits between the Earth and the sun will appear as either a morning star or an evening star (but never as a star of full night).

Scarcely any literary texts from the third millennium B.C. are known to exist, and I certainly did not expect that it would be possible to trace the astral character of Inanna/Ishtar any further back than, say, to the dynasty of Akkad (ca. −2350). However, a routine check of the Assyriological literature that deals with the earlier periods revealed something surprising.

The oldest known written documents on Earth have been excavated in Uruk (Mesopotamia), which happens to be also the principal place of worship of Inanna. These documents belong to the first part of the third millennium. They represent a very early stage in the art of writing and are therefore not yet fully decipherable, but about half of the signs have survived to later stages of the cuneiform script and can be identified without doubt. Tablets excavated at level IV (the deepest level containing written documents) sometimes juxtapose the symbols "star" and "Inanna." Since the star symbol is used as a determinative before names of gods in later times, this might mean nothing more than "goddess Inanna." But a tablet from level III has at its end "star, Inanna, rising sun," and another has "star, setting sun, Inanna" (Figure 2).[7] The two texts appear to be lists of offerings. The subscripts obviously have something to do with astronomy, but the exact meaning is open to interpretation. Falkenstein suggests that the offerings were made on the occasion of the heliacal rising or setting of the star of Inanna, that is, when the star of Inanna was first or last visible before or after its conjunction with the sun. In the light of the passage concerning Inanna's descent that I quoted above, it is perhaps even more plausible that these offerings were made to Inanna as the morning or evening star, respectively. Finally, according to Falkenstein, an (unpublished?) tablet from level IIIb appears to mention a "feast on the day when the star of Inanna sets."[8]

Figure 2. Archaic tablets from Uruk. No. 65 (level IV) shows the symbols "star, Inanna." No. 606 (level III) shows "star, setting sun, Inanna." (From A. Falkenstein, *Archaische Texte aus Uruk,* Leipzig, 1936.)

Taken together, these archaic texts constitute evidence that Venus, the star of Inanna, was known shortly after the year −3000 and quite likely was already known in its dual manifestation as the morning and evening star.

Old-Babylonian and Later Evidence for the Planet Venus

We shall consider here the famous Venus observations made in the time of Ammizaduga, king of Babylon, which are contained in the omen series "Enuma Anu Enlil," named after the first words on the first tablet of the series. An "omen series," as used here, refers to a multitablet collection of texts, and consists, essentially, of a long list of pairs of events— "if *X* . . . , then *Y* . . ."—which allow the reader to infer the probable future occurrence of *Y* if *X* has been observed. Such an omen series may cover many different types of events; the *X*'s can be features of the liver of sacrificial animals, malformed births, unusual behavior of animals, or astronomical or meteorological phenomena, and the *Y*'s can vary also over a broad range: weather, crops, personal fortune, domestic and foreign affairs, and so forth. Astrological omina tend to be of a public nature, since the stars stand over the entire land.

The sixty-third tablet of the "Enuma Anu Enlil" series contains omina which are based on actual observations of the planet Venus, here called Ninsianna ("Bright queen of heaven"). To facilitate this discussion, we shall reproduce a portion of the text in translation (Figure 3). The subdivision into paragraphs is ancient, but the year numbers (counting from the beginning of the text) and other comments in parentheses are modern.[9]

The text covers twenty-one consecutive years, apart from two interruptions. The first interruption is short: instead of some observations and the second omen for year 8, the text inserts the Old-Babylonian year formula ("Year of the Golden Throne"). The other interruption is longer: it displaces the observations of year 18 and reveals a primitive scheme for calculating Venus phenomena that is based on somewhat unrealistic constant periods of invisibility (7 days at inferior and 3 months at superior conjunction). The actual periods of invisibility of the planet Venus when it passes between the Earth and the sun (inferior conjunction) and when it lies on the far side of the sun from the

Figure 3. The Venus tablets of Ammizaduga, years 5 to 9

(Year 5) If on IX 25 (var.: 12) Venus disappears in the east, remaining absent in the sky 2 months 4 days, and on XI 29 (var.: 16) Venus appears in the west, the harvest of the land will be successful.

(Year 6) If on VIII 18 (var.: 28, "20 newly broken") Venus disappears in the west, remaining absent in the sky 3 (var.: 5) days, and on IX 1 appears in the east, hunger for grain and straw will be in the land; desolation will be wrought.

(Year 7) If on V 21 Venus disappears in the east, remaining absent in the sky 2 months 11 days, and on VIII 2 Venus appears in the west, there will be rains in the land; desolation will be wrought.

(Year 8) If on IV 25 Venus disappears in the west, remaining absent in the sky 7 days, and on V 2 Venus appears in the east, there will be rains in the land; desolation will be wrought.

If on XII 25 Venus disappears in the east.

Year of the Golden Throne.

(Year 9) If on III 11 Venus disappears in the west, remaining absent in the sky 9 months 4 days, and on XIII 15 appears in the east, king shall send greetings (var.: declaration of war) to king.

Earth (superior conjunction) vary considerably for different seasons of the year, since the sun and Venus rise and set differently (with relation to the horizon) as the seasons change. The periods of invisibility range from 1 to 18 days at inferior conjunction and from 55 to 70 days at superior conjunction, even without taking into account the chance fluctuations caused by unfavorable weather conditions.

Unfortunately, it is all too clear that the text of the tablets under consideration is very corrupt and contains many scribal errors. This can be seen from:

(1) Internal inconsistencies (between the dates of disappearance and reappearance and the duration of invisibility). A few of these can be resolved with the aid of a duplicate text, as in year 6, but three serious cases of inconsistency (among 22) remain.

(2) Disagreements between duplicates, often of minor size (±1 day), but sometimes serious ones, as in year 5.

(3) Astronomical impossibilities, as in year 9, where Venus disappears twice in a row without appearing in between, and where the time of invisibility at inferior conjunction in month XII should be about four days, instead of nine months and four

days. In this particular case, it seems that appearance (day 11 of month III) and disappearance (day 11 of month XII) in the west had been compressed into a single event very early on, before the duration of invisibility had been added to the text. That the durations of invisibility are later additions is suggested by the fact that these periods of time are based on a schematic month of 30 days, instead of the true lunar month, which alternates irregularly between 29 and 30 days.

Kugler[10] had recognized the year formula in year 8 of the text: only one year bearing the name "Year of the Golden Throne" is known, and it happens to be the eighth year of King Ammizaduga of Babylon, who reigned for twenty-one years. This suggests that the observations in question cover the reign of Ammizaduga. This attribution receives firm establishment from the pattern of intercalated months, that is, months inserted into the calendar to keep it in step with the seasons.

Years with Intercalary Months

The significance of the intercalations has been overlooked by both Velikovsky and Rose.[11] In fact, the intercalary months allow quite a stringent test not only of the attribution of the Venus tablets to Ammizaduga, but also of what Rose calls the "astronomers' dogma."

The Babylonian calendar is based on the true lunar month: the month begins on the evening when the new moon first becomes visible. Thus, the length of the month varies irregularly between 29 and 30 days; twelve lunar months correspond to about 354 days. In roughly every third year, the Babylonians inserted an additional (thirteenth) month in order to keep the month names in step with the seasons.

Before about −500, these intercalations were handled in a rather haphazard fashion by royal decree. We have the original tablet of a revealing letter of King Hammurabi (one and one-half centuries before Ammizaduga) to governor Siniddinam of Larsa: "To Siniddinam speak: thus [says] Hammurabi: The year has an intercalary month. The coming month shall be written as a Second Ululu [month VI_2]. And instead of what has been said that the taxes should arrive in Babylon on the 25th Tishrit [month VII], they shall arrive on the 25th of the second Ululu."[12]

The additional month was inserted either in the middle of the year as a Second Ululu (month VI_2) or at the end of the year as a Second Adaru (month XII_2).

For Ammizaduga's reign we have seven or eight intercalary months that are attested to by tablets dated during an intercalary month (these tablets record commercial contracts between individuals). The seven intercalary months are 4A, 5U, 10U, 11U, 13A, perhaps 14U,[13] 19U, and 20A, where A stands for a Second Adaru (in the years 4, 13, and 20), and U stands for a Second Ululu (in the years 5, 10, 11, 14, and 19). The last two intercalations can be shifted somewhat. We know for certain only that among the last five years of Ammizaduga's reign, two consecutive years contained a U-intercalation followed by an A-intercalation. Thus the pattern of intercalation in these years must be one of the four possibilities 17U, 18A; 18U, 19A; 19U, 20A; or 20U, 21A (see Kugler,[14] and Reiner and Pingree[15]).

The paragraph above describes the intercalations of which we can be certain from sources other than the Venus tablets. The Venus tablets, on the other hand, attest directly to the intercalary months 11U and 19U. If we want to obtain a decent alignment of the intervals of invisibility with regard to the mean synodic period of Venus (about 19.8 months), we must insert five more intercalary months into the period covered by Ammizaduga tablets. The synodic period is the time interval required for Venus, the Earth, and the sun to regain the same positions relative to one another, so that Venus will appear again on the sky in the same position relative to the sun as it had one synodic period earlier. When we examine the Venus observations and determine where the intercalary months must be inserted to make these observations consistent with the synodic period of Venus, we find that the months that we must insert in the period covered by the tablets are as follows: 4A or 4U; 5U; 9A or 10U; 13U or 13A or 14U (depending on whether one follows the main text or a variant for year 13); and 20A or 20U.

The remaining years must have been regular ones with no intercalary months.

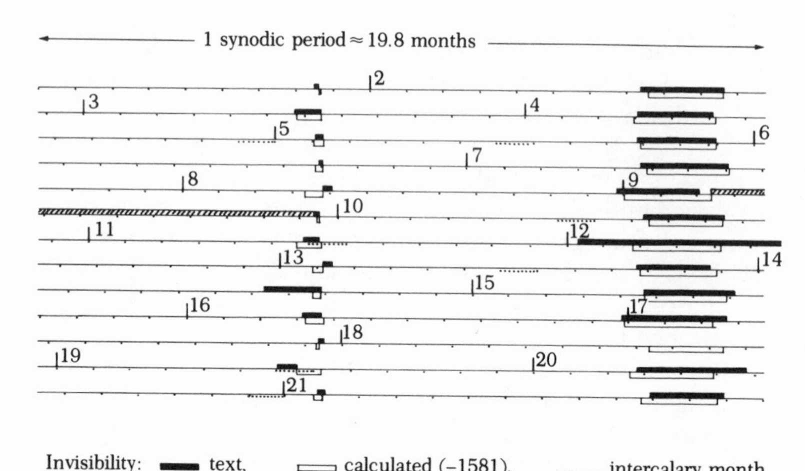

Figure 4. Synodic period of Venus and intercalary months. (In explanation, imagine a cylinder whose circumference is one synodic period of Venus [19.8 synodic months], with the 21 years covered by the Venus tablets wrapped around it; align the periods of invisibility vertically, by inserting a few intercalary months at the appropriate places; then, in the end, slit the cylinder open and spread it out.)

When we compare these five calculated intercalary months with the intercalary months that appear in tablets dated during an intercalary month, we find remarkable agreement. All of the intercalary months calculated from what we know of Venus' orbital motion today (those listed at the end of the preceding paragraph) match with intercalary months that are attested by the tablets recording commercial contracts. As for the intercalary months 11U and 19U, they are both required from the standpoint of Venus' orbital motion and are recorded in the Venus as well as the contract tablets. The odds against finding such good agreement by chance between the intercalations in the tablets and those called for by the present value of the synodic period of Venus are greater than one thousand to one. If this agreement is not due to chance, it fixes the date of the Venus observations in the reign of Ammizaduga, and in addition demonstrates that the relationships of the lengths of the month, the year, and the synodic period of Venus must have been substantially the same as they are now.

For a more detailed verification of the observations recorded in the tablets, we should also show that the Venus data—apart from scribal errors—are compatible with modern calculations. Unfortunately, we do not know precisely when Ammizaduga reigned, so we can, at best, show that the time range allowed by today's historians contains acceptable solutions.

The Date of Ammizaduga's Reign

Some thirty years after the reign of Ammizaduga, the Hittite king, Mursili I, raided Babylon and put an end to the First Dynasty of Babylon. Afterwards, Babylon was ruled by Kassite kings, but we do not know by how much the earlier part of the Kassite dynasty overlapped with the First Dynasty of Babylon. Therefore, while Near-Eastern chronology is well established (to within a few years) back to about −1450, and while the internal chronology of the eight hundred years between the reign of Sargon of Akkad and Mursili's raid on Babylon is also in good shape, there is a gap of uncertain length (some fifty to two hundred years) between the two periods. If Ammizaduga could be dated accurately through the astronomical records that survive from his reign, we would gain almost a millennium of accurately known chronology.[16]

Venus phenomena (for example, the day on which Venus is first visible after inferior conjunction) repeat themselves fairly accurately after eight years, except that the dates in the lunar calendar decrease by four days on the average. Thus, if Venus was first visible after inferior conjunction on the day of the full moon eight years ago, it will now be first visible four days before full moon. After 56 or 64 years, the Venus phenomena will again be in the same relation to the phases of the moon, and thus to the lunar calendar (±2 days), but they will now occur about half a month earlier with respect to the solar year. Because of this approximate periodicity, the astronomical data on the planet Venus can furnish only a set of possible dates as to when the observations were made. A selection must be made among this set on the basis of historical evidence, perhaps with some assistance from statistics. The quality of the data is such that systematic shifts of ±2 days should be detectable, so that we may be able to rule out movement of the possible date by 56 or 64 years on the basis of the quality of the observational evidence.

Nowadays, only four solutions are thought to be more or less compatible with both history and astronomy. These are: year 1 of Ammizaduga began in −1701, in −1645, in −1637, or in −1581. Of these four possibilities, −1701 leads to improbably long average reigns for a series of Hittite kings, while a date below −1581 would make these same reigns impossibly short.[17]

All previous investigations of the problem of dating Ammizaduga's reign from the Venus observations[18] share a serious common weakness having to do with the calculation of the dates of the first (or last) visibility of Venus following (or preceding) its conjunctions. These dates have been calculated on the assumption that Venus is visible on a particular evening or morning if the sun is at least a certain number of degrees, designated by h_o (see Figure 5), below the mathematical horizon at the moment when the planet passes through the horizon. The "mathematical" horizon is that which would exist if the Earth's surface were perfectly smooth, without regard to topographic features such as hills, mountains, trees, and so on.

Neither the value of h_o, nor the ways in which it might have varied with changing atmospheric conditions, have been reliably known. However, it is now possible to bypass this difficulty by comparing the old observations with a set of Late-Babylonian values for h_o (called the *arcus visionis* since the time of Claudius Ptolemy). I scanned the published Late-Babylonian observational texts and found a hundred usable Venus observations, dating from −461 to −73.[19] The details of this investigation are given in the Appendix to this chapter; the results can be summarized as follows.

Among the four proposed chronologies, the middle two must

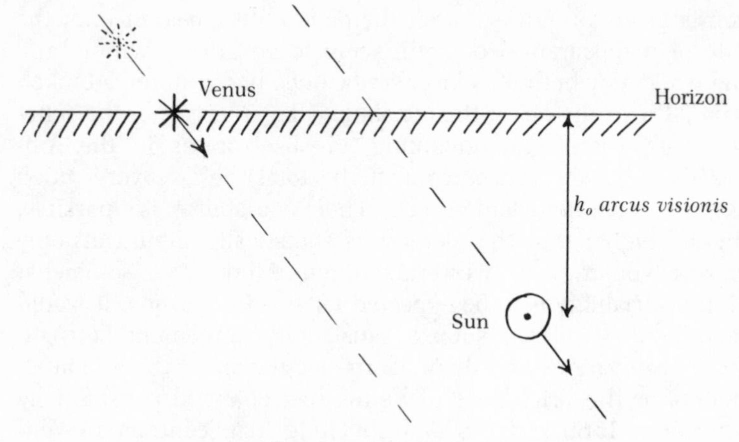

Figure 5. Arcus visionis

be rejected for statistical reasons with about 0.1 percent probability of error. For −1645, the observed dates are systematically too early (by two days on the average) in comparison with the calculated dates, and this for all four types of events (first or last visibility in the morning or evening). For −1637, the situation is reversed, and the observed dates are systematically too late. The other two chronologies pass the statistical tests for shift (Wilcoxon) with flying colors. In view of the historical evidence,[20] the short chronology (−1581) is most likely correct.

We might pause to notice that when systematic shifts of only ±2 days in records thirty-five hundred years old become strikingly visible in such a consistent fashion, then all but the hardiest skeptics should be convinced that the core of Venus data agrees well with modern calculation, using the present orbital elements for the motion of Venus.

To sum up the observations recorded in the Ammizaduga tablets, I would say that of the 50 dates given in the tablets, 9 are impossibly deviant for any chronology (these are presumably scribal errors), and 6 more are marginal. For about half of these errors, one can find plausible explanations. For instance, in all three cases where the period of invisibility at inferior conjunction is given as 7 days, either the date of disappearance, or the date of reappearance, or both, seem to be grossly wrong, and one wonders whether a clever scribe once had restored a broken original with the aid of the constant 7-day intervals of the schematic insertion. The remaining 35 observations in the Ammizaduga tablets (70 percent of the total) behave very much like the Late-Babylonian set. Their variability is, possibly, slightly higher, but the increase is statistically significant only for one type of event (western settings). Moreover, a somewhat higher variability is to be expected for several reasons. It would be difficult to obtain such a satisfactory agreement between these observations and the modern calculations if the orbital elements or the brightness of Venus had changed substantially between −1560 and −500. I conclude that, contrary to Velikovsky's hypothesis, the Venus data from the reign of Ammizaduga is compatible with modern orbital elements within the limits of Babylonian observational accuracy.

Appendix: *Technical Details*

Astronomical Calculations

The calculations referred to in the text have been based on the same orbital elements, and on essentially the same choice of perturbations of these planetary orbital elements, as were used by Tuckerman in his calculation of planetary tables;[21] they were performed on the CDC 6400/6500 computer of the Federal Institute of Technology (ETH) in Zürich. The beginning of the month (first visibility of the lunar crescent) was calculated according to C. Schoch's formulas from the position of the moon at the time of sunset.[22] I have checked this method on the 170 lunar crescents available[23] through LBAT 1387+*1388 (a Venus text for the years −462 to −433 which also gives the month lengths), and have found perfect agreement of the calculated visibility with the observed visibility in 163 cases. This agrees with Schoch's success rate (95 percent for 400 cases). In view of this excellent agreement, the dates calculated, using Schoch's formulas, were employed throughout this work.

The Late-Babylonian Venus Observations

In the observational texts accessible to me, 121 first and last visibilities of Venus could be located. Among these, thirteen bear the remark "not observed" (presumably because of poor weather), and I eliminated eight more because the observational nature of their respective texts has been doubted (among these are LBAT **1477 = Strm. Camb. 400 and LBAT **1478 = CBS 11901). Thus, one hundred observed events remained, dating from −461 to −73.

Within this span of time, there seem to be changes in the practice of observing or of reporting the observations, and there are differences between the treatment of first and last visibilities.

Last visibility. Early texts give a unique date; later texts give two dates, the first one with a measured duration of shining. For example (LBAT **1237, 110 S.E.): "Month VII 15: 9° shining of Venus. On the 19th Venus set in the west in Libra." Very late texts give a unique date, without duration of shining. Did this arise from a decay of observational practice?

First visibility. Early texts usually give two (or three) dates. For example (LBAT 1387, Artaxerxes I., year 2): "Month XII_2. . . . On the 6th in the east in Aries it appeared high (IGI NIM), it appeared (IGI) on the 4th or 5th." Later texts add a duration of shining. For example (LBAT 375, 144 S.E.): "Month II. . . . On the 18th Venus appeared brilliant and high (IGI KUR NIM A) in the east in the end of Taurus; 9°30′ was its shining. It appeared (IGI) on the 15th."

The duration of shining is the interval between planet-rise and sunrise (or sunset and planet-set), expressed in time degrees (1° equals four minutes of time). These time intervals are quite accurate: in 24 out of 32 cases, the discrepancy with modern calculation is less than 1°; these calculations assumed a horizontal refraction of 34′ and were made for the upper limb of the sun (semidiameter 16′).

Curiously, first appearance proper (IGI without qualifications) is always reported *after* the measured one (otherwise, the astronomical diaries adhere to a strict chronological order). Does this represent the educated guess of the observer? The occasional vagueness "on the 4th or 5th" would seem to support this opinion. Or did the observer wait for the reports of luckier observers elsewhere?

If two dates are given, I shall distinguish them as "inner" and "outer" (i.e., nearer to and farther from the date of conjunction with the sun). I believe that the "outer" date denotes the day when the planet was last/first visible so close to the horizon that the duration of shining could be measured. The "inner" date for a first visibility seems to denote the day when the planet was first visible at all, and may occasionally be based on an educated guess of the observer. For a last visibility, however, it denotes the first day when the planet was *invisible*, as we shall see below. If only one date is given, it corresponds to the "inner" date, and in fact the "inner" date only is retained in the summary sections of the Babylonian astronomical diaries.

Table 1 summarizes the *arcus visionis* values (the negative altitude of the sun when Venus is on the mathematical horizon) for the Late-Babylonian observations. WS, ER, ES, and WR are abbreviations for western setting, eastern rising, etc.; WS-1 is the day before western setting, and so forth.

These tables (called stem-and-leaf displays by J. W. Tukey) should be read as follows: Among the "outer" observations for WS, there is no value between 5.0 and 5.9; there is one value between 6.0 and 6.9, namely 6.4; and there are three values between 7.0 and 7.9, namely 7.0, 7.1, and 7.6. Some extreme values which cannot be represented by this scheme are indicated by asterisks (e.g., Table 4, where two WS-values are smaller than 1.0).

Among the extreme values, a few are suspicious also for other reasons (e.g., the date is damaged on the tablet). These values are in italic in Table 4.

At WS and ER (inferior conjunction), the *arcus visionis* changes by 0°.6 to 1°.6 per day. At ES and WR (superior conjunction), the daily changes are between 0°.1 and 0°.3.

It can be seen from Table 1 that the WS-values (except the "outer" ones) are suspiciously low, much lower than the ER-,

Table 1. Arcus visionis of Venus in Late-Babylonian texts

"Outer" Observations

	WS	ER	ES	WR
5.				678
6.	4		2	789
7.	016	2468	0024888	22359
8.	44	0002222356		
9.	7	249		
10.	5	4		
11.		1		

"Inner" Observations

	WS	WS-1	ER	ES	ES-1	WR
2.	8					
3.	69		2			
4.	6	3	6			
5.	334	156	5678	8899	9	234
6.		258	0128	588	0018	0144578
7.	1	8	1225	14	0137	35
8.	8		013			
9.			*1*			
10.		*3*				

"Unique" Observations

	WS	WS-1	ER	ES	ES-1	WR
2.	*0*					
3.	1388	6				
4.	00267	177		68	9	
5.	369	04448	778	0689	028	7889
6.		349	8	13346	0135559	124455
7.		5		3	5	1249
8.			8			
9.						
10.						

"Not Observed"

	WS	ER	ES	WR
1.		0		
2.	57			
3.				
4.	99	9	6	
5.	056		017	
6.		7	0	124
7.	6			1
8.		5		
9.				

ES-, and WR-values. This is precisely what is to be expected, if WS and ES correspond to first invisibility instead of last visibility. Therefore, I also calculated the *arcus visionis* for the preceding day (WS-1, ES-1). The *arcus visionis* value for WS-1 is still somewhat lower than that for ER (since one knows where to look for the planet).

The behavior of the "inner" and of the "unique" observations is very similar, and after checking this with Wilcoxon's test, I have pooled them (first column of Tables 4 and 5).

Table 2 compares C. Schoch's values of the *arcus visionis* with the values determined here. Schoch's values are surprisingly accurate; they are all just inside the 95 percent confidence level for the median values. Since Schoch's values are intended to be used as limits, above which the planet is on the average visible, one might argue that they should be compared not to the median values but rather to the medians decreased by half of the average daily change; the agreement then becomes even better. (I prefer medians to means, because for asymmetric and long-tailed distributions they are both more robust and also easier to interpret.)

Table 2. Median values of the *arcus visionis*

	WS	WS-1	ER	ES	ES-1	WR
Median	4.4	5.5	6.1	6.1	6.3	6.4
Median minus one-half of daily change		5.0	5.6		6.2	6.3
Schoch's limit	5.2 (WS and WS-1)		5.7	6.0 (ES and ES-1)		6.0

A closer scrutiny of the first columns of Tables 4 and 5 shows that the distributions tend to be asymmetric, since, as a rule, the lower quartile is nearer to the median than the upper quartile. The sample sizes are not large enough to draw very precise conclusions, but the distributional evidence can be roughly summarized as follows. In approximately 75 percent of the cases

WS occurs within −2 and +1 days of the "ideal" date (corresponding to the median *arcus visionis* value);

ER occurs within −1 and +2 days of the "ideal";
ES occurs within −6 and +4 days of the "ideal";
WR occurs within −4 and +6 days of the "ideal."

The remaining 25 percent of the cases are about equally distributed to the left and to the right of these intervals.

The Venus data for ES and WR suggest that the *arcus visionis* value is somewhat higher in fall and winter than in spring and summer, perhaps by as much as 1°, but the data are insufficient for an accurate determination of seasonal effects. We hope that the combined evidence from all planets will ultimately allow such a determination (Peter Wirth is currently working on the Jupiter data).

Comparison between Late-Babylonian and Ammizaduga Data

The Ammizaduga data are more than one thousand years older than the oldest Late-Babylonian data we have, and they may not correspond to the same observational conventions and standards. But at least the terminology of the schematic insertion makes it clear that also in the Ammizaduga data "disappearance" really denotes the date of first invisibility ("until IX 6 she will stand in the east, on IX 7 she will disappear"), not the date of last visibility.

One can surmise that the Old-Babylonian astronomer would not as easily postulate a nonobserved appearance/disappearance when the sky was clouded, since he would lack his Late-Babylonian colleague's knowledge of how to predict it accurately. Note in this connection the text LBAT 1251 (−179 April), which states: "Month I 15 setting of Venus in the east in Aries; from the 14th on, while observed, not seen." If this conjecture is true, the roughly 10 percent of nonobserved Late-Babylonian events would correspond to an equal percentage of unusually high *arcus visionis* values among the Ammizaduga data—assuming that bad weather prolongs the period of invisibility.

Moreover, we are extrapolating our astronomical theories beyond safe grounds by the same one thousand years. For instance, the inaccurately known variations in the rate of rotation of the Earth might easily add up to a clock-time error of a few hours. This would destroy the excellent (95 percent) agreement between the calculated and the observed lunar crescents, and is equivalent to the introduction of additional random errors (with a standard error ≤ 0.5 days; since the clock-time error affects the visibility of the moon and of Venus in the same way, it does not cause any perceptible systematic errors).

I have tried to avoid and to eliminate any conscious or subconscious doctoring of the evidence. If available, I have used the dates of the best text (in the order W.1924.802; reverse of K.2321 + 3032; K.160). Some conjectures (namely 9 III 11 WR, 20 VI 1 WR, and the data for year 18) were calculated but not used in the displays and the statistical tests. An *arcus visionis* value calculated for an event recorded on the Venus tablets can be seriously "wrong" because of a scribal error, an observational blunder, or a wrong astronomical theory. No automatic judgment is implied, but only the presence of the first type of errors is proven. The approximate periodicity of the phenomena (five synodic periods in eight years) is clearly visible in any case.

Table 3 shows the raw computer output, while Tables 4 and 5 summarize the *arcus visionis* values for the four chronologies −1701, −1645, −1637, and −1581.

Of the fifty phenomena recorded on Ammizaduga's tablets, nine are so seriously wrong that they do not fit into the limits of Tables 4 and 5. These nine were omitted:

Year	8	IV	25	WS	(7-day pair)
Year	8	V	2	ER	
Year	12	I	9	ES	
Year	12	VI	25	WR	
Year	13	II	5	WS	(member of 7-day pair)
Year	14	VII	10	WS	
Year	19	VI_2	1	WS	
Year	19	VI_2	17	ER	
Year	21	I	27	WS	(member of 7-day pair).

Of these nine, four are members of the three WS and ER pairs with seven days of invisibility. Perhaps here a damaged

ONG= 44.50, GLAT= 32.50 BAFYLON

CUS VISICNIS OF VENUS AND ITS DAILY CHANGE

						-1701	-1645	-1637	-1581
ZOG	1	XI	15	VS WS	VAR. 25(RESTORED FROM INTERVAL)	5.54-1.58	10.31-1.52	3.71-1.57	9.98-1.50
ZOG	1	XI	18	VS ER	VAR. 28	5.88 .75	4.33 .87	8.13 .84	4.88 1.00
ZOG	2	VIII	11	VS ES		7.78 -.26	8.42 -.25	7.56 -.25	7.72 -.24
ZOG	2	X	19	VS WR		7.17 .27	6.26 .27	7.12 .27	6.17 .26
ZOG	3	VI	23	VS WS		9.65 -.59	8.79 -.60	5.78 -.68	5.73 -.74
ZOG	3	VII	13	VS ER		4.46 1.62	1.69 1.63	7.28 1.58	5.91 1.56
ZOG	4A	IV	2	VS ES	TEXT HAS VII; CORR. FROM INTERVAL (WR-2M1D)	6.98 -.16	6.68 -.12	6.03 -.14	5.70 -.11
ZOG	4A	VI	3	VS WR		5.22 .11	5.4[illegible] .12	5.89 .12	6.07 .14
ZOG	5U	II	2	VS WS		-.37-1.53	4.77-1.55	-1.89-1.57	3.04-1.59
ZOG	5U	II	8	VS ER	SIC,BUT INCOMPATIBLE WITH INTERVAL(18D, 15D)	3.78 .84	2.69 .76	6.05 .69	5.54 .66
ZOG	5U	IX	25	VS ES	VAR. 12, 24(RESTORED FROM INT.)	5.41 -.22	6.54 -.25	5.81 -.25	7.00 -.27
ZOG	5U	XI	29	VS WR	VAR. 16, 28	6.65 .27	5.50 .27	6.65 .27	6.08 .27
ZOG	6	VIII	28	VS WS	VAR.18(SCRIBAL ERROR,INT. AND ER O.K.)	5.25-1.33	6.20-1.17	2.09-1.15	2.95 -.98
ZOG	6	IX	1	VS ER		7.59 1.31	3.28 1.46	8.09 1.44	5.59 1.55
ZOG	7	V	21	VS ES		6.94 -.25	7.66 -.25	6.55 -.25	7.29 -.24
ZOG	7	VIII	2	VS WR		6.26 .21	5.86 .17	6.43 .18	5.94 .14
ZOG	8	IV	25	VS WS		-13.99 -.94	-10.46-1.16	-15.39-1.07	-13.40-1.24
ZOG	8	V	2	VS ER		17.46 1.16	11.86 1.17	16.49 1.03	12.14 .99
ZOG	8	XII	25	VS ES		6.42 -.13	6.76 -.16	6.27 -.16	7.14 -.20
ZOG	9	III	2	VS WR	RESTORED FROM INTERVAL (ES+2M7D)	4.01 .24	3.35 .26	4.19 .26	3.50 .27
ZOG	9	III	11	VS WR	CONJECTURE (=DATE OF WS)	6.06 .21	5.64 .24	6.42 .23	5.89 .26
ZOG	9	XII	11	VS WS	TEXTS HAVE III, INT. 9M4D, AND OMIT WR	6.68-1.57	9.89-1.52	3.30-1.57	9.55-1.50
ZOG	9	XII	15	VS ER		6.27 .76	5.54 .88	9.35 .83	6.19 1.01
ZOG	10U	VIII	10	VS ES	VAR. 8(RESTORED FROM INT.)	6.92 -.26	7.81 -.25	6.70 -.25	7.10 -.24
ZOG	10U	X	16	VS WR		7.51 .27	6.32 .27	7.45 .27	6.47 .26
ZOG	11U	VI	26	VS WS		4.50 -.70	3.70 -.72	.96 -.75	1.51 -.81
ZOG	11U	VI2	8	VS ER	VAR. 7; WR(SCRIBAL ERROR)	1.96 1.64	-.80 1.63	4.83 1.60	3.43 1.58
ZOG	12	I	9	VS ES	VAR. 8	11.21 -.07	10.66 -.10	10.38 -.10	10.66 -.14
ZOG	12	VI	25	VS WR		12.52 .20	11.85 .15	12.34 .16	11.93 .12
ZOG	13U	II	5	VS WS		-11.30-1.44	-6.58-1.54	-12.99-1.43	-6.90-1.54
ZOG	13U	II	12	VS ER		10.25 .68	8.73 .63	11.38 .54	10.22 .54
ZOG	13U	IX	21	VS ES	CR X; INTERVAL(16D) INCOMPATIBLE, BUT VAR. 2M	5.43 -.22	6.83 -.26	5.83 -.25	7.01 -.27
ZOG	13U	XI	21	VS WR	VAR.11; INT.(16D) INCCMPATIBLE, BUT VAR. 2M	5.36 .27	4.49 .27	5.37 .27	4.81 .27
ZOG	14	VII	10	VS WS	VAR. 11	34.57 -.01	29.63 .03	28.96 -.02	24.33 -.05
ZOG	14	VIII	27	VS ER	VAR. 26, 28	6.62 1.34	3.69 1.47	10.00 1.43	7.72 1.54
ZOG	15	V	20	VS ES	VAR. 21	6.32 -.25	6.80 -.25	5.94 -.25	6.47 -.24
ZOG	15	VIII	5	VS WR	VAR. IX	7.58 .23	6.97 .19	7.78 .20	7.18 .16
ZOG	16	IV.	5	VS WS	VAR. VIII 4	2.59-1.05	8.01-1.06	3.46-1.18	8.51-1.21
ZOG	16	IV	20	VS ER	VAR. WR	7.45 1.37	2.04 1.32	7.53 1.22	3.75 1.14
ZOG	16	XII	25	VS ES	VAR. 15	5.98 -.13	6.27 -.16	5.78 -.15	6.38 -.19
ZOG	17	III	21	VS WR	CR 24; UNCERTAIN AND INCOMPATIBLE WITH INT.(3M9D)	8.73 .16	8.60 .20	9.29 .19	9.14 .22
ZOG	17	XII	11	VS WS		-.07-1.58	3.30-1.57	-1.80-1.55	3.08-1.52
ZOG	17	XII	15	VS ER	RESTORED FROM INTERVAL (WS+4D)	9.64 .70	9.35 .83	12.18 .77	10.52 .96
ZOG	18	IX	12	VS ES	WEIR'S CONJECTURE (P.27)	5.54 -.26	6.20 -.25	5.09 -.25	5.51 -.24
ZOG	18	XI	16	VS WR	WEIR'S CONJECTURE (P.27)	8.39 .27	7.45 .27	8.59 .27	7.54 .26
ZOG	19U	VI2	1	VS WS		15.48 -.35	15.41 -.38	13.56 -.46	14.97 -.48
ZOG	19U	VI2	17	VS ER	VAR. 14	-22.90 1.25	-24.71 1.17	-19.10 1.36	-21.19 1.27
ZOG	20A	III	25	VS ES		6.70 -.16	6.28 -.12	5.63 -.14	5.33 -.11
ZOG	20A	VI	1	VS WR	VAR.24,14. 1 IS RESTORED FROM INTERVAL(2M6D)	5.97 .11	6.11 .12	6.67 .11	6.93 .13
ZOG	20A	VI	24	VS WR	VAR. 14; INCOMPATIBLE WITH INTERVAL (2M6D)	8.46 .12	8.55 .10	9.06 .10	9.40 .09
ZOG	21	I	27	VS WS	VAR. 26; INTERVAL 7D	-5.71-1.52	-.73-1.58	-7.41-1.53	-1.03-1.59
ZOG	21	II	3	VS ER		6.11 .77	5.74 .69	8.12 .63	7.68 .61
ZOG	21	X	28	VS ES	RESTOREC FROM INTERVAL (WR-2M)	3.17 -.19	4.17 -.22	3.50 -.22	4.65 -.25
ZOG	21	XII	28	VS WR		8.39 .27	7.26 .27	8.40 .27	7.57 .27

ble 3. Raw computer output. Each line gives the Babylonian date (year, month, day), the event S WS = Venus western setting), some comments, then the calculated *arcus visionis* (negative alude of the sun when the planet is in the horizon) and its daily change, for each of four chronoloes (Year 1 starting in –1701, –1645, –1637, and –1581, respectively).

Table 4. Arcus visionis values of Venus, inferior conjunction

	Late-Babylonian	−1701	−1645	−1637	−1581
		WS			
< 1.		**		**	
1.				0	5
2.	*08*	6		1	
3.	136889		37	357	001
4.	002679	5	8		
5.	333469	25		8	7
6.		7	2		
7.	1				
8.	*8*		08		5
9.		6	9		6
10.			3		0
		WS-1			
< 1.				**	
1.		25		7	
2.					3
3.	*6*	6		2	9
4.	1377		49	69	66
5.	01444568	2		3	
6.	234589	6	3	5	5
7.	58	1	4		
8.		2			
9.			14		7
10.	*3*	2			
11.			48		05
		ER			
< 1.			*		
1.			7		
2.		0	07		
3.	2	8	37		48
4.	6	5	3	8	9
5.	5677788	9	57		569
6.	012488	136		0	2
7.	125	46		35	77
8.	0138		7	111	
9.	*1*	6	*4*	4	
10.		2		0	25
11.				*4*	

archetype had been restored with the aid of the schematic insertion (which has constant seven-day intervals at inferior conjunctions).

Of the remaining observations, five extremal ones look suspicious also, for other reasons:

Year	9	III	2	WR	(restored from interval; possibly refers to year 17)
Year	13	II	12	ER	(member of 7-day pair)
Year	17	III	21	WR	(incompatible with interval)
Year	17	XII	15	ER	(restored from interval)
Year	20	VI	24	WR	(incompatible with interval)

In Tables 4 and 5, these are in italics. The statistical tests were performed twice, once with and once without them.

A glance at Table 4 shows that for −1637, the *arcus visionis* values for WS and ER are too low and too high respectively, while for −1645 the situation is reversed. This is confirmed by Wilcoxon's test for shift.

Table 6 gives a summary of these tests, namely the normalized Wilcoxon test statistics.

It can be seen from Table 6 that for −1645 the observed dates are systematically too early, and for −1637 systematically too late, and this for all four types of events. The combined evi-

Table 5. *Arcus visionis* of Venus, superior conjunction

	Late-Babylonian	−1701	−1645	−1637	−1581
		ES			
3.		2		5	
4.	68		2		6
5.	06888999	44		68889	37
6.	13345688	034799	3357888	0367	45
7.	134	08	78	6	001137
8.			4		
		ES-1			
3.					
4.	9				
5.	0289				
6.	00011355589				
7.	01357				
8.					
		WR			
3.			*4*		5
4.		*0*	5	2	8
5.	2347889	24	459	49	9
6.	0112444455578	36	33	46	1125
7.	12345*9*	256	03	148	26
8.		457	*66*	4	
9.				*13*	*14*

Table 6. Summary of Wilcoxon tests*

Events	Sample sizes		Year −1701		Year −1645		Year −1637		Year −1581	
	Late-Babylonian	Ammizaduga	Test statistic	Probability of chance variation	Test statistic	Probability of chance variation	Test statistic	Probability of chance variation	Test statistic	Probability of chance variation
WS	22	8	+0.09	93%	−1.88	6.0%	+2.63	0.9%	−0.12	90%
ER	23	11	−0.02	98%	−2.52	1.2%	+2.61	0.9%	−0.50	62%
ES	21	11	−0.58	56%	−2.08	3.7%	+0.46	65%	−1.37	17%
WR	26	11	+1.23	22%	−0.52	60%	+1.56	12%	+0.18	86%
Combined	92	41	+0.36	72%	−3.50	0.05%	+3.63	0.03%	−0.90	37%

**Explanation*. Take the column with −1645 on top. In the first line we test the hypothesis that −1645 is the correct chronology by testing whether the 22 Late-Babylonian and the 8 Old-Babylonian *arcus visionis* values have the same distribution. We do this with the aid of Wilcoxon's test (see for instance E. L. Lehmann, *Nonparametrics: Statistical Methods Based on Ranks* [San Francisco: Holden-Day, 1975], pp. 5ff.). In this particular instance the Wilcoxon test statistic, normalized to have mean 0 and variance 1, takes on the value −1.88. The negative sign indicates that the Old-Babylonian dates are too early on the average (higher *arcus visionis* values, cf. Table 4). But the deviation might be due to chance: if the hypothesis is correct, the probability is 6 percent that the absolute value of the Wilcoxon statistic is 1.88 or larger. Note the four minus signs: for all four kinds of events the Old-Babylonian dates tend to be somewhat early. In the bottom row, the evidence is combined. The halved sum of the four test statistics, $-3.50 = (-1.88 - 2.52 - 2.08 - 0.52)/2$, is normal with mean 0 and variance 1 *if* the hypothesis is true. The probability that its absolute value is 3.50 or larger by chance is 0.05 percent. Hence, on the combined evidence, we can confidently reject the chronology −1645; the chances of error are smaller than one in 1,000 (about 1 in 2,000, to be precise).

dence allows us to reject these two chronologies with a probability of error smaller than 0.1 percent. This confirms van der Waerden's earlier results.[24]

Of course, the rejection of the middle two chronologies also depends on the accuracy of the orbital elements. But one would need relatively large systematic errors (about 1° in the heliocentric longitude) to tilt the balance.

The other two chronologies (−1701 and −1581) pass the Wilcoxon test for shift with flying colors. If the suspicious data are omitted, the results (not shown here) are in all essential respects the same.

The 36 observations which remain after the removal of the nine "seriously wrong" and the five "suspicious" values behave very much like the Late-Babylonian set. Apart from two or three somewhat high *arcus visionis* values (which were anticipated), only the following visible anomalies remain: (1) one (−1581) or three to four (−1701) impossibly low *arcus visionis* values; (2) a gap in the middle of the Ammizaduga WS values, which (for −1581) contains three quarters of the Late-Babylonian values, and which corresponds to a (statistically significant) higher variability of the old WS values.

(For the sake of completeness, I have also checked some of the older solutions. Among them, −1856 fits well, while −1800 and −1808 must be rejected. The minimum rejection levels are, respectively, −1976: 5 percent; −1920: 4 percent; −1856: 40 percent; −1800: 0.13 percent; −1808 was not recalculated, since it is clear that it gives a worse fit than −1800 does. Among the historically impossible later solutions, I should mention −1517, −1482, and −1426, with minimum rejection levels of 18 percent, 5 percent, and 6 percent, respectively.)

Conclusion

The chief results of this long and very technical section can be summarized as follows. We have shown with the aid of appropriate statistical methods that the middle two chronologies (Ammizaduga Year 1 = −1645 or −1637) are not compatible with the Venus data, and that the disagreement exhibits a very systematic and coherent pattern. Since systematic shifts of only about ±2 days are involved, this shows perhaps better than anything else that the Venus data, although distorted by scribal errors, still contain a substantial hard core of good, bona-fide observations. On the other hand, both the long (−1701) and the short (−1581) chronologies agree very well with the data (the short one fits slightly better, but the difference is not decisive). In particular, we have shown that, contrary to Velikovsky's suggestions, the Venus data are compatible with modern orbital elements, within the limits of Babylonian observational accuracy.

Note

During the revision of the manuscript, a definitive new edition, *The Venus Tablet of Ammisaduqa,* by Erica Reiner and David Pingree,[25] became available (henceforth cited as RP). The sources have been increased from the seven texts known to Langdon-Fotheringham-Schoch (cited as LFS)[26] to twenty. Unfortunately, the new fragments often add to the confusion by offering new scribal variants, but RP also corrects some of Langdon's misreadings. Some new information concerning the intercalary months could be worked into the main text, but since I did not have the time to redo all the astronomical-statistical calculations, I could not and did not update the "Technical Details." It appears that eight lines of Table 3 can be improved, thanks to RP, as follows:

Year 5U II 8. The tablet has a clear II 18 (error in Langdon's copy, Plate III).

Year 9 III 2. This line should be deleted. RP associates this omen with year 17 (omen 58).

Year 13U IX 21 and 13U XI 21. The best readings for these two lines seem to be 13A X 21 and 13A XI 21 respectively, with several variants. Compare RP (p. 23) for the intercalation, and note that Langdon reads "21 on the tablet clearly" (LFS, p. 8[10]).

Year 16 XII 25. RP gives only XII 15.

Year 17 III 21. RP gives III 25, with variant III 4.

Year 17 XII 11. RP has XII 10.

Year 17 XII 15. RP has XII 14.

In comparison to the calculated values, some of the fits are improved, some are worsened. The influences of the changes tend to cancel each other, and we can confidently expect the overall conclusions to stay unchanged, even without repeating all the calculations.

Surely, this is one of the worst data sets I have met as a statistician, but still, Pingree's comments on the quality of the data in the second and third 8-year periods (RP, pp. 21f.) in my view are overpessimistic (possibly he was influenced by the somewhat overzealous "cleaning" performed by van der Waerden). In my revised count based on RP, the three 8-year periods of the text would contain, respectively:

(1)	16 good,	0 questionable,	3 bad values;
(2)	15 good,	2 questionable,	5 bad values;
(3)	4 good,	1 questionable,	3 bad values;
Total:	35 good,	3 questionable,	11 bad values.

Here, "good" means that the data agrees fairly well with the calculated values, within the limits of Babylonian observational accuracy, "bad" means gross discordances for any chronology fitting the majority of the data, and "questionable" refers to the murky region in between.

Notes

1. I. Immanuel Velikovsky, *Worlds in Collision* (New York: Doubleday, 1950).
2. *Ibid.* pp. 348–349.
3. D. O. Edzard, in H. W. Haussig, *Wörterbuch der Mythologie* (Stuttgart: Klett, 1963) I, p. 81ff.
4. J. B. Pritchard, *Ancient Near Eastern Texts Relating to the Old Testament*. 3d ed. (Princeton, N.J.: Princeton University Press, 1969), p. 52ff. Sumerian text in *Proc. Amer. Philos. Soc.* 85:293–323, 1942.
5. The most recent translation, by D. Reisman, *J. Cuneiform Studies* 25:185, 1973, has "radiant" or "solitary" in place of "strange."
6. A. Falkenstein und W. von Soden, *Sumerische und Akkadische Hymnen und Gebete* (Zürich: Artemis Verlag, 1953), p. 90ff.
7. A. Falkenstein, *Archaische Texte aus Uruk* (Leipzig: Harassowitz, 1936), Texts Nos. 65, 602, and 606. I am grateful to E. Sollberger for pointing out the potential significance of these texts.
8. *Fischer Weltgeschichte,* Bd. 2 (Frankfurt a.M.: Fischer, 1965), p. 52. Writing about the Neo-Sumerian period (ca. −2000), H. Sauren claims: "Il est évident que les offrandes étaient faites le jour oú la planète disparaissait et celui où elle réapparaissait" ("Les fêtes néo-sumériennes et leur périodicité," *Actes de*

la XVIIe Rencontre Assyriologique Internationale [1970], p. 25). (I am indebted to W. W. Hallo for this reference; it does not seem to me, however, that Sauren has really proven the point.)

9. S. Langdon, J. K. Fotheringham, and C. Schoch, *The Venus Tablets of Ammizaduqa* (London: Oxford University Press, 1928).

10. F. X. Kugler, *Sternkunde und Sterndienst in Babel, II* (Münster, 1909), pp. 280ff.

11. L. E. Rose, Babylonian Observations of Venus, *Pensée* 3:18–22, 1973.

12. R. Frankena, *Briefe aus dem British Museum,* in F. R. Kraus, ed., *Altbabylonische Briefe* (Leiden: E. J. Brill, 1966), Letter No. 14.

13. The 14U intercalation could not be verified by Erica Reiner and David Pingree, *The Venus Tablet of Ammisaduqa* (Malibu, Calif.: Undena Publications, 1975), and is quite possibly wrong. See also Note, p. 142, with respect to new fragments reported in Reiner and Pingree.

14. Kugler, *Sternkunde und Sterndienst in Babel,* II, p. 61.

15. Reiner and Pingree, *The Venus Tablet of Ammisaduqa,* p. 23.

16. See for instance the article by M. B. Rowton in *The Cambridge Ancient History,* 3rd ed., I, Part 1 (Cambridge: Cambridge University Press, 1970).

17. According to A. Kammenhuber, *Die Arier im Vorderen Orient* (Heidelberg: Winter, 1968), the Hittite and Mitanni-Hurri evidence favors the short chronology (–1581) and is incompatible with the long one (p. 40[95]).

18. Convenient summary in B. L. van der Waerden, "Die Berechnung der ersten und letzten Sichtbarkeit von Mond und Planeten und die Venustafeln des Ammisaduqa," *Berichte der Math.-Phys. Klasse der Sächsischen Akademie der Wissenschaften zu Leipzig,* 94. Band (Leipzig: 1943), pp. 23–56. See also B. L. van der Waerden, *Die Anfänge der Astronomie* (Groningen: P. Noordhoff Ltd., ca. 1965). The recent monograph by J. D. Weir, *The Venus Tablets of Ammizaduqa* (Leiden: Nederlands Instituut voor het Nabije Oosten, 1972), is methodologically unsound; it places too much weight on a few arbitrarily selected observations.

19. A. Sachs, *Late Babylonian Astronomical and Related Texts, copied by T. G. Pinches and J. N. Strassmaier* (Providence R.I.: Brown University Press, 1955). This basic publication of cuneiform texts (quoted as LBAT) also contains an exhaustive catalogue of all known observational texts. P. Wirth (University of Zürich) kindly let me use also his finds from independent searches through the same material.

20. See A. Kammenhuber, *Die Arier im Vorderen Orient.*

21. B. Tuckerman, *Planetary, Lunar and Solar Positions, Memoirs of the American Philosophical Society,* LVI and LIX (Philadelphia: 1962, 1964).

22. P. V. Neugebauer, *Astronomische Chronologie* (Berlin and Leipzig: 1929), Table E 21.

23. A. Sachs, *Late Babylonian Astronomical and Related Texts.*

24. B. L. van der Waerden, "Die Berechnung der ersten und letzten Sichtbarkeit von Mond und Planeten und die Venustafeln des Ammisaduqa."

25. Erica Reiner and David Pingree, *The Venus Tablet of Ammisaduqa.*

26. See S. Langdon, J. K. Fotheringham, and C. Schoch, *The Venus Tablets of Ammizaduqa.*

5 Planetary Astronomy and Velikovsky's Catastrophism*

DAVID MORRISON
Institute for Astronomy
University of Hawaii

Introduction

Since the publication of *Worlds in Collision* in 1950,[1] Immanuel Velikovsky and his supporters have argued that the oral traditions and historic records of ancient man indicate that planetary encounters and near collisions involving Earth, moon, Venus, and Mars took place between twenty-five hundred and thirty-five hundred years ago. They further assert that a great deal of physical evidence from both geology and astronomy is not only consistent with these catastrophes but provides positive support for this reconstruction of history.[2] However, most physical scientists (particularly astronomers) have taken strong exception to the Velikovskian claims, and a desultory debate has continued for a quarter of a century. Although rarely agreeing on much else, both parties to the dispute have asserted that Velikovsky's theories should be accepted, rejected, or modified on grounds of scientific evidence, not on the basis of philosophical, mystical, or religious belief. His ideas have been presented as scientific, and both Velikovsky and his supporters have repeatedly begged that they be tested by the usual rules of scientific enquiry. It is in this spirit that I shall discuss the evidence that has accumulated from study of the moon and planets

* This paper is based on an invited address given in 1974 at the McMaster University symposium on "Velikovsky and the Recent History of the Solar System," organized by the editors of *Pensée*.

that bears upon the question of recent catastrophic interplanetary encounters.

I should emphasize at the outset that the issue of conflict between Velikovsky and orthodox astronomy and geology is *not* catatrophism *per se*. It is obvious that the surfaces of the moon and planets have been scarred by tremendous explosions resulting from meteoric impacts; and terrestrial geologists have increasingly recognized in recent years the dominant role of sudden and violent events, such as volcanic eruptions and massive flash floods, in molding the surface of the Earth. Even in the field of celestial mechanics, there is no doubt about the occurrence of collisions among asteroids today, and among many more planetesimals at the time the solar system was forming. Further, it is not clear whether the orbits of the planets have always been where they are today, or whether subtle gravitational and tidal effects might not over hundreds of millions of years have altered the shapes of orbits significantly. The problem with Velikovsky's hypothesis is one of *time scales*. He would condense what most would regard as a billion years of solar-system history into a few centuries. Mountain ranges that geologists believe took a hundred million years to form were thrown up, according to Velikovsky, within a few days; the moon bubbled, and meteorites cratered its surface, while our ancestors watched; planets changed orbits from one year to the next, confounding the astronomers of China and Babylon. Such hypotheses strike at the foundations of astronomy and the Earth sciences, suggesting as they do that entire disciplines, such as geological dating, Newtonian celestial mechanics, and lunar geology are founded in illusion and pursued in error. It is this concept of *exceedingly recent catastrophism* that separates Velikovsky so dramatically from the mainstream of science.

I do not believe either Velikovsky or the majority of his followers understand how revolutionary his thesis is. They insist that, although his paradigm is different, his theories are basically compatible with existing science. As an example, Velikovsky in the Epilogue to *Worlds in Collision* goes so far as to express the belief that "the theory of cosmic catastrophism can, if required to do so, conform with the celestial mechanics of Newton," and the pages of *Pensée* (a pro-Velikovsky journal published between 1972 and 1974) have been filled with claims that results of the space program provide one verification after another of Velikovsky's ideas. I have no reason to doubt the sincerity of such sentiments. Where the subject matter is complex and the relevant information is buried in jargon-filled scientific journals it is understandable that a nonscientist should fail to realize the gulf that separates Velikovsky from the scientific world. Perhaps the present volume will help to bridge that gulf and to put the Velikovsky phenomenon in perspective.

Although both Velikovsky and his critics appeal to rational scientific debate to settle their differences, in practice it often appears that the two sides do not have the same understanding of this process. Much of the difficulty arises from the scope and novelty of Velikovsky's ideas. He has chosen single-handedly to attack the fundamental precepts of physics, astronomy, geology, and archaeology, relying not on a chipping away at the edges of conventional thought, but rather on a broad, frontal assault on the whole fabric of mid-twentieth-century science. His approach is eclectic, depending for its impact on the daring of its multidisciplinary synthesis rather than on a detailed, scholarly criticism of any one area. Further, Velikovsky's writings have all been directed at a lay audience, and he frequently uses language for effect rather than precision. For instance, when he discusses the polar caps of Mars, his interchangeable use of the terms carbohydrates, hydrocarbons, and carbon compounds leaves a careful reader totally confused as to his meaning, as do the similarly interchanged terms crater, ring-forming feature, and bubble used in discussions of the lunar surface. This imprecision of language is one of the greatest difficulties facing anyone who tries to understand Velikovsky.

Let us try, however, to give Velikovsky's ideas the dispassionate criticism he seeks. By a long process of trial and error, scientists have developed a methodology for testing new ideas or modifications that are claimed to improve upon old ones. The process works something like this. First, the new theory is expected to be consistent with well-verified previous observations and experiments. Thus, for instance, Einstein's theory of gravitation was formulated from the beginning to be equivalent to the Newtonian theory under everyday circumstances—as it had to be, considering the superb precision with which Newtonian mechanics explained such phenomena as planetary motions. Second, the new theory is required to be sufficiently precise and quantitative in areas where it differs from previous ideas, both to verify its consistency with what is already known and to elucidate those areas in which it differs from previous ideas. In this way the new theory generates a set of predictions that can be tested in an effort to verify that it is, indeed, a better approximation to reality than the ideas it is to replace. Third, it is assumed that even one definitive observation or experiment in the area where the predictions of the two theories differ is sufficient to reject one or the other. (This is not to say the one theory is right and the other wrong, in an absolute sense, but only that nature seems more consistent with the one than with the other.) Finally, it is of the essence of science that investigation and testing of the new theory be carried out openly and that results be judged by those familiar with the areas under discussion, usually through presentations at meetings and by the publication of papers in scholarly journals.

Practically nothing in either Velikovsky's theories or the reactions of scientists to them conforms to this idealized picture. First, because the scope of his ideas is so broad, he has never attempted to demonstrate their consistency with the vast amount of relevant data and interpretation. Instead, he has been highly selective in the data he has chosen to discuss and has largely ignored the work of others. Further, his theories are not quantitative, and hence they do not lend themselves to being tested by observation or experiment as readily as one might hope. The very fact that arguments have been going on for twenty-five years over what Velikovsky meant when he characterized Venus as "hot" amply testifies to this point. Indeed, his work is so dependent on ancient historical material that it generates very few possibilities for carrying out tests of its present validity. For instance, his catastrophist scenario for planetary motion requires the action of forces not seen to influence planetary motion today, yet he has never established what these forces were or how they operated. Consequently, no tests of his ideas in the realm of celestial mechanics can be carried out. Finally, of course, his work has not been couched in the language of quantitative science. Thus, most scientists have not considered his work worthy of their interest or attention, and no constructive interaction has taken place.

In spite of the difficulties discussed above, it seems worthwhile to try to identify those areas where semiquantitative predictions can be made from Velikovsky's theories and to determine how well these predictions survive a comparison with observation and experiment. This chapter deals with only one small part of the consequences of the Velikovsky thesis: the physical effects on the planets and the moon of the Jovian birth of Venus and subsequent interplanetary encounters. Does the evidence favor the theories of Velikovsky, is it neutral, or does it conflict with them? An answer to this question is required if we are to evaluate the many claims and counterclaims made concerning the astronomical basis of Velikovsky's theories.

In discussing this evidence I have tried, wherever possible, to deal with Velikovsky on his own terms. For instance, I have not criticized in those areas for which he has never published a clear statement of his views—such as the mechanism whereby Venus was expelled from Jupiter. I have focused on the three broad areas in which the Velikovskian theory asserts that recent catastrophic encounters among the planets will have *observable* consequences. The first is in the chemistry of the planets, which is said to have been influenced by the Jovian origin of Venus and by atmospheric interchanges among Venus, Earth, and Mars. The second is in the thermal structure of these bodies, which would be modified by massive recent heating, a theory that has led Velikovsky to suggest that Venus, Mars, and the moon all have significant internal heat sources. The third is in the surface morphology of these bodies, which would have been modified by catastrophic impacts, volcanism, and possibly large-scale crustal melting at the time of the encounters. I will consider each of these areas in turn, after first briefly discussing the more general proposal that electromagnetic effects have had a major influence on the moon and planets.

Electromagnetism in the Solar System

Central to Velikovsky's scenario for the recent history of the solar system is a rapid evolution of planetary orbits, from a situation in which near encounters were taking place less than three thousand years ago among Venus, Earth, moon, and Mars, to the present situation, in which these objects all follow stable, well-separated, near-circular orbits. It is a simple fact of life that these planets do not today threaten to leave their places and approach their neighbors, and that they have been following their present paths with great precision at least since the observations made by the ancient Greeks and compiled in the second century A.D. by Claudius Ptolemy. What were these strange forces that, acting twenty-five hundred years ago, so greatly influenced planetary motion but now appear to be dormant? Velikovsky has most frequently suggested that they were electromagnetic.

Electromagnetism is a well-understood branch of physics, and its effects on planetary motion can be calculated and found to be inconsequential today, consistent with astronomical observations. Unfortunately for Velikovsky, no one has shown any way they could have been important in the past either, although a serious effort was recently made by Michelson.[3] Yet Velikovsky and his supporters continue to invoke this concept and to castigate all of their critics who fail to take electromagnetic effects into account. The Velikovskians begin with the contention that electromagnetism can generate important forces (certainly true), but jump then to the conclusion that these forces must be taken into account in explaining past (but not present) planetary motions. How this can happen is not explained, and thus we are left with no hope of testing the assertion. Meanwhile, it appears from the Velikovskian literature that every discovery of electromagnetic effects in the solar system, from the magnetic field of Mercury to the Van Allen belts of Jupiter to the curved paths of solar prominences, is somehow a vindication of Velikovsky. The fact that these phenomena have no effect on planetary motions is ignored.

One suggestion that frequently appears in the pro-Velikovsky literature is that the forces—electromagnetic or of some unknown origin—that so influenced the planets during their encounters act only at very close range. Thus these forces would be undetectable today, when the planets are far from each other, but are hypothesized to have dominated the situation at times of near collision. However, even this *ad hoc* hypothesis cannot save the situation. Somehow, the orbits of the planets had to evolve from a configuration occurring twenty-six hundred years ago (at a time when Venus could encounter Mars and Mars could encounter Earth) into their present orbits, which they certainly had attained by two thousand years ago. Planetary orbits are closed curves: under the influence of gravitation alone, orbits once intersecting will continue to do so. If, by hypothesis, the nongravitational forces required by Velikovsky act at short range only, then these forces cannot have been available to circularize the orbits *following* the last encounter. The suggestion that these forces could be consistent with present planetary behavior as a result of their short range provides no way to explain the rapid evolution from intersecting the near-circular orbits required by Velikovsky's scenario. This objection holds whether or not the effects were electromagnetic.

Velikovsky's most famous invocation of planetary electromagnetism came in 1953, when he predicted that Jupiter would prove to be a source of radio signals.[4] Less than a year later decametric radio radiation from Jupiter was discovered, and at a much higher level of intensity than had been expected by most investigators. According to the Velikovskian literature, this episode was a classic case of a prediction by an unpopular scientific theory that was subsequently verified, thus "proving" the correctness of the new theory. The real interpretation is, however, more ambiguous.

Velikovsky's prediction was apparently based on his conviction that electromagnetic fields existed on Jupiter and that, in the dynamic milieu of the Jovian atmosphere, kinetic energy should be transformed into electromagnetic radiation. This train of logic is a good one, and it is to Velikovsky's credit. However, his correct intuition was never developed into a "theory," nor was it formulated as an alternative to some pre-existing theory that predicted an *absence* of radio radiation from Jupiter. Velikovsky also never suggested what the radio radiation he expected should be like: for example, its wavelength, spectrum, intensity, frequency of occurrence, and so on. Thus, the subsequent detection of the phenomenon in no way provides a test of any electromagnetic theory of Jupiter or of planets in general. Even more to the point at issue, electromagnetic effects in Jupiter's atmosphere are, as noted above, really irrelevant to Velikovsky's scenario of planetary catastrophism. Since there is no indication that electromagnetic effects can significantly influence planetary motions, and certainly the electromagnetism inherent in the Jovian decametric radio sources cannot do so, this prediction of Velikovsky's has no bearing on any of the central issues in dispute with conventional science.

Some supporters of Velikovsky would claim that it is unfair to expect the creation of a quantitative theory of electromagnetic effects on planetary motion from a medical doctor with little background in the physical sciences. They would emphasize that Velikovsky's point is that many lines of evidence from the historical record indicate that planetary encounters *did take place* in recent times, and the absence of an adequate theory to account for these encounters does not negate the evidence that they occurred. I am willing to concede this point, and to drop the whole question of why these catastrophes took place. In the remainder of this chapter I will concentrate exclusively on the evidence for and against planetary encounters and avoid speculation as to their cause. However, in return we should expect Velikovsky and his supporters to stop claiming that every evidence of electromagnetic effects in astronomy is somehow an indication of the correctness of Velikovsky's thesis of near-colliding worlds just three thousand years ago.

Cosmochemical Considerations

The Jovian birth of Venus is central to Velikovsky's theories, and the possible similarities of the two planets based on their common origin are discussed extensively in *Worlds in Collision* and subsequent writings. If Venus were born of Jupiter, she would be expected to have a similar composition, or at least a composition that might reasonably have evolved from a Jovian base within a few thousand years. In one of his better-known predictions, Velikovsky suggested on the basis of such arguments that the atmosphere of Venus should be rich in hydrocarbons. I will return below to the problem of the Venerian atmosphere but will first consider the bulk compositions of the two planets.

The mass of Jupiter is 318 times that of the Earth, and its mean density is 1.3 g cm^{-3}; these two facts alone give important clues to its bulk composition. The low density implies that most of its mass is in the form of light elements, of which the cosmically most abundant are hydrogen, helium, neon, argon, oxygen, nitrogen, and carbon. The very large mass of the planet indicates high interior pressures and consequent compression of the material; when this information, together with data on the compressibility of materials, is taken into account, it is clear that most of the interior of Jupiter is hydrogen and helium, which are also the two most abundant elements in stars. Many additional observations, particularly of the shape and gravity field of the planet and of its thermal-energy emission, further constrain the models of the interior of the planet. Recent models, based on data from the Pioneer flybys of Jupiter,[5] suggest that the main bulk constituent is hydrogen, which undergoes a phase transition from gas to liquid at a depth of about 1,000 km and from ordinary liquid to a conductive, "metallic" liquid at a depth of about 25,000 km. The temperature rises with depth, reaching about 30,000°K near the center. A rocky or metallic core with a mass of a few times the mass of the Earth is compatible with the observations, but such a core of heavy elements can amount at most to a very small percent of the total mass of

Jupiter. All measurements and calculations are consistent with a composition for this planet that is not significantly different from that of the sun.

That the bulk composition of Venus is entirely different is indicated by its density of 5.1 g cm^{-3}, similar to that of the Earth and a factor of four greater than that of Jupiter, in spite of its smaller mass and the smaller compressional forces in its interior. There is no way an object of the mass and density of Venus could contain significant amounts of hydrogen or helium, and even moderately light elements such as oxygen, carbon, and nitrogen must be less abundant than the cosmically common heavy elements, such as sulfur, silicon, aluminum, iron, and nickel. The exact composition and structure of the interior of Venus is less well specified than that of Jupiter, as a result of a paucity of relevant observations and of the less diagnostic behavior of refractory minerals and metals at high pressures, compared to the lighter elements. The most comprehensive recent theoretical work is by John Lewis of the Massachusetts Institute of Technology.[6] Combining the direct observations with more general consideration of likely chemical scenarios for the formation of the terrestrial planets, he suggests that the core of Venus is a nickel-iron alloy and the mantle is ferromagnesian silicates. Independent of any model, however, is the conclusion that Venus, like Earth, is composed of a core of metals and a mantle of rocky minerals. One must conclude that the bulk chemistry of Jupiter and Venus could hardly be more different.

Velikovsky does not discuss the problem of the incompatible bulk compositions of Jupiter and Venus, but he does devote considerable attention to the atmosphere of Venus. Evidence from spectroscopy, from photometry of occultations of stars, and from the Pioneer flybys, shows that the Jovian atmosphere is chemically dominated by hydrogen and its most abundant simple compounds: methane, ammonia, and water. Methane is, of course, the simplest hydrocarbon, and recent evidence suggests that several higher hydrocarbons are also present in very small amounts in the upper atmosphere of Jupiter.[7]

In contrast to that of Jupiter, the atmosphere of Venus is oxidized. Observations employing high-resolution spectroscopy (optical and radio) and spacecraft radio occultations, and direct sampling accomplished by the Venera series of atmospheric entry probes, show that the Venerian atmosphere consists almost entirely of carbon dioxide, with small amounts of water (the amount is in dispute), nitrogen, and argon, and with trace quantities of hydrochloric and hydrofluoric acid. At the surface of the planet, the pressure approaches 100 atmospheres.[8]

Although the composition of the atmosphere has been known for many years, the composition of the visible clouds of Venus has eluded astronomers until recently. By 1972, a wide range of observations had defined the visible and infrared reflection spectrum of the clouds, their temperature, the size and sphericity of the particles, their refractive index, and the approximate vapor pressure of water near their tops, yet no material had been identified that matched this well-established set of properties. In an exciting example of scientific detective work, several researchers then independently found the answer, namely, that the visible clouds of Venus are composed of sulfuric acid droplets at between 75 percent and 85 percent concentration.[9] Because of the long list of highly diagnostic properties that had been assembled from previous observations, this identification appears to be secure. On the other hand, there is no evidence of hydrocarbons in the clouds or in any other part of the visible atmosphere of Venus; in particular, the absence of the strong spectral band near 3.5 micrometers that is produced by the C-H bond common to all hydrocarbons sets stringent upper limits of a few parts per million on the quantity of hydrocarbons that could be present.[10] The unfortunate report in the press a decade ago that the Mariner 2 spacecraft had detected hydrocarbon clouds on Venus is apocryphal.[11] There is thus no evidence of the hydrocarbons predicted by Velikovsky. This does not seem to me to be as strong an argument against a Jovian origin for Venus as is provided by the bulk composition, however, since the atmosphere represents a negligible fraction of the mass of Venus, and it is possible to imagine substantial atmospheric evolution on a time scale as short even as a few thousand years.

Velikovsky asserts that there were atmospheric exchanges between Venus, Earth, and Mars, resulting in the addition of Venerian hydrocarbons to Earth and Mars and of Martian argon and neon to Earth. On this basis, he predicted that the polar caps of Mars were composed of hydrocarbons and that a substantial fraction of the atmosphere of Mars would consist of argon and/or neon.[12] Let us investigate these two predictions for Mars.

At the time that Velikovsky first suggested that the polar caps of Mars might be composed of hydrocarbons, there was little direct evidence concerning their composition. Most astronomers assumed, by analogy with Earth, that the polar caps were water ice, while a minority argued for a composition of solid carbon dioxide (dry ice). The first direct and unambiguous data on their composition were provided by the infrared radiometer experiment on the Mariner 6 and 7 flybys in 1969, which showed that the temperature of the evaporating edge of the cap corresponded to the vaporization temperature of carbon dioxide and was incompatible with water ice. Subsequent thermal and spectroscopic evidence confirms that the bulk of the caps are carbon dioxide but that the "remnant" caps that survive through the Martian summer consist of water ice.[13] In contrast, the spectroscopic upper limits on the amount of hydrocarbons that might be present are a few parts per million.[14]

When *Worlds in Collision* was written, the only gas identified in the atmosphere of Mars was carbon dioxide, but neither the amount of this gas nor the total bulk of the atmosphere had been measured. By the mid-1960's a combination of spacecraft radio studies and improved spectroscopy carried out with Earth-based telescopes had shown that the surface pressure on Mars was less than one percent that on Earth and that carbon dioxide was by far the dominant gas. The consensus on the eve of the first direct measurements, carried out by the Viking landers in 1976, was that a minimum of 80 percent of the atmosphere was carbon dioxide, thus leaving at most 20 percent of such spectroscopically inactive gases as nitrogen, argon, or neon.[15] At the same time, Velikovsky continued to predict that argon and neon would be found to be the primary components.

Experiments on the Viking landers settled this issue. Carbon dioxide was found to make up 96 percent of the atmosphere, with 2.5 percent nitrogen and 1.5 percent argon.[16] Very small amounts of oxygen, krypton, and xenon were also detected. Thus Velikovsky's assertion that argon and neon were major components of the Martian atmosphere was clearly contradicted.

In summary of this section, Velikovsky's predictions that the clouds of Venus and the polar caps of Mars are hydrocarbons, and that the atmosphere of Venus contains hydrocarbon gases and the atmosphere of Mars is primarily argon and neon, are all incorrect. Further, the concept of planets being born one from another and shifting back and forth in their orbits seems basically inconsistent with the regularities in bulk composition that are increasingly apparent as we learn more about the chemistry of the planets. Velikovsky's record in this arena is certainly not encouraging.

Thermal Considerations

During the encounters hypothesized by Velikovsky, internal stresses and the dissipation of tidal forces on the planets would have heated their interiors, and Venus is claimed to have been "candescent," by which I presume Velikovsky means a temperature above about 1100°C, at which point rocks would radiate significant thermal energy at visible wavelengths. In *Worlds in Collision* and subsequent writings, he concludes that both Venus and Mars have measurable internal heat sources; that is, both planets radiate significantly more heat than they absorb from the sun. He has advanced a similar argument more recently for the moon. Much has been made in writing about Velikovsky of these "predictions" and their supposed verification, especially in the case of Venus. However, these claims are not supported by the facts.

Let us first consider Mars. From the Mariner 6, 7, and 9 spacecraft and from the Viking orbiters, thermal emission from a large fraction of the surface has been mapped in broad infrared bands near wavelengths of 10 and 20 micrometers, and the data have been carefully analyzed in terms of the thermal properties of the surface.[17] As a consequence, the thermal behavior of this planet is the best understood of any except Earth and moon. All of the temperatures are consistent with equilibrium conditions; there is no indication of an internal heat source. Obviously, this point is not crucial to Velikovsky's theory, and in *Worlds in Collision* it is clear that his discussion of excess radiation from Mars is presented in accordance with his understanding of the thermal observations that were available in 1950, rather than that he was making a prediction. However, as recently as June 1974 Velikovsky publicly reiterated that Mars has a thermal excess, and for that reason I mention the point here. On what basis Velikovsky concluded that the early measurements suggested anomalously high temperatures is not clear; as reviewed in 1960, for instance, the data from the 1920's and 1930's all gave subsolar temperatures on Mars of 273°K to 300°K, which are in excellent agreement with both theoretical expectations and modern spacecraft data.[18]

Heating of the moon, as well as Mars and Venus, is a natural consequence of Velikovsky's theory; the significance of this event for the lunar surface morphology will be discussed below. Velikovsky never suggested that the high temperatures beneath the lunar surface that would result from this heating would be observable from Earth, but in 1969 he proposed that they would be revealed by the subsurface temperature gradient.[19] Subsequent heat-flow measurements conducted on the Apollo 15 and 17 missions indicated a flux of only 15–20 erg cm^{-2} s^{-1}, which is lower than the average terrestrial value.[20] The corresponding temperature gradient is very shallow and suggests that the temperature does not reach the melting point of rock until a depth of hundreds of kilometers below the lunar surface. Apollo seismic studies also confirm this great thickness for the lunar crust. The data thus fail to show the predicted effect, and indeed they preclude the possibility of a substantial fraction of the lunar crust having been molten within the last few million years.

That Venus has a "hot" surface and a large internal heat

igher than would be maintained by solar heating alone. Thus
ven this elementary calculation, carried out on the basis of
elikovsky's own suggestions for Venus, shows that after three
housand years of cooling there would not be enough heat con-
ucted from the interior to come close to accounting for the
igh surface temperature of the planet.

None of the above arguments contradict Velikovsky's basic
esis of planetary encounters, since they simply indicate that
e present temperature of Venus is relatively insensitive to con-
tions on that planet three thousand years ago. But they do
ow that Velikovsky can make no claim in favor of his ideas
om the high surface temperature of Venus. His original
ggestion of a hot Venus was based on an erroneous interpre-
tion of existing temperature data and is not a consequence of
s catastrophist thesis.

served cooling

Velikovsky, as noted in the previous section, appeared to be-
ve Venus was still cooling at an approximately linear rate
om its high temperature three thousand years ago. Writing in
66, he proposed as a "crucial test of [his] theory" that Venus
ould be cooling at a rate of a fraction of a degree per year, and
t this rate of cooling should be measurable over a period of a
cade or two. In 1972 he quoted three infrared measurements
the cloud temperatures that appeared to support this predic-
n.[24] Unfortunately, there exist other published measure-
nts that do not indicate cooling of the clouds,[25] and, indeed,
en the different spectral regions sampled and the poor cali-
tions available for the older data, it is not surprising that
se observations do not show such an effect. In addition, re-
t studies[26] indicate that the cloud-top temperature is con-
led by the freezing point of sulfuric acid and by the deposi-
of solar energy, and is therefore insensitive to variations in
surface temperature. More relevant would be a consider-
n of the many *microwave* observations published during the

source is perhaps the most widely quoted prediction made by Velikovsky. Repeated measurements of the cloud-top temperatures at a variety of infrared wavelengths, including those from the recent Mariner 10 flyby, however, verify that the total energy radiated from Venus is equivalent to that from a black body of about 230°K, or just what one would expect in the absence of any internal energy source.[21] Thus there is no evidence that Venus radiates more energy than it receives from the sun. The temperature in the lower atmosphere and at the surface is, of course, much greater. Such a state of affairs was occasionally suggested in the period 1930 to 1957, by, for instance, Rupert Wildt of Yale, and of course by Velikovsky. The actual surface temperature, which turned out to be higher than any model had predicted, was first measured in microwave radiation in the late 1950's, and directly by the Venera 7 surface lander in 1970;[22] these and numerous other studies show that the surface temperature is 750 ± 20°K over the entire planet. An important problem of planetary studies during the past decade has been to understand the mechanism that produces this high surface temperature.

Velikovsky argued that Venus was hot, in part on the basis of observations published before 1950, which showed that the cloud-top temperature did not vary from day to night; he inferred that such a state would be a natural consequence of an internal heat source that dominates the energy balance of the planet. An alternative explanation of the observed absence of diurnal temperature variation is that the atmosphere might be so massive that it effectively damps out the diurnal variations in received solar radiation. The two explanations differ in their predictions concerning the overall heat balance, and the fact that the observed cloud temperature is equal to the equilibrium value is inconsistent with the explanation given by Velikovsky; rather, it is clear that a massive atmosphere must play a vital role in the thermal affairs of Venus.

The response of planetary astronomers to the discovery of the 750°K surface temperature of Venus has been to develop numerical greenhouse-effect models that account for the high temperature in terms of equilibrium processes. The problem of calculating the atmospheric structure and surface pressure for a planet with a massive atmosphere and thick clouds is difficult, and the results—particularly in regard to the surface temperature—are often sensitive to the quantities of quite minor constituents of the atmosphere. In the case of Venus, those who have carried out such calculations agree that the temperature at the surface must be hundreds of degrees higher than the cloud-top temperature. Most recent work, in fact, finds no difficulty in reproducing the observed 750°K, particularly when a fraction of a percent of water vapor is permitted in the lower atmosphere. These conclusions from greenhouse calculations were strengthened by the Venera 8 measurement that about 1 percent of the solar illumination penetrates to the surface of the planet.[23] This amount of radiation deposited at the base of the atmosphere is, according to most calculations, sufficient to maintain a stable greenhouse effect. In summary, most students of the problem find that the known properties of the Venerian atmosphere are such as to produce a greenhouse effect of the magnitude needed to give a surface temperature of 750°K without invoking an internal heat source.

Because the surface temperature of Venus plays so large a role in both Velikovsky's ideas and the mythology that surrounds them, it is appropriate to analyze some of the claims in the pro-Velikovskian literature in more detail. Discussion of four specific problems follows.

THE MAXIMUM COOLING RATE

Velikovsky's scenario for the recent history of Venus places its surface temperature in the range of incandescence about thirty-five hundred years ago as a result of its recent Jovian birth, its close passages to the sun, and its violent interactions with the Earth. It is the thermal reservoir established at that time that he asserts to be the source of the high temperature on Venus. Although Velikovsky never describes in detail how fast he thinks the planet cooled, there is an implication in his writing that he assumes an approximately linear drop in temperature. Such an

assumption is, however, in contradiction to wha
the cooling of planets, which must take place
heat to space. Even a simple dimensional solu
tion that describes the conduction of heat throu
uid crust and its subsequent radiation to spac
cooling *rate* is proportional to the *sixth power*
ture (expressed in degrees Kelvin). Thus, ir
2250°K to the present 750°K, which is a factor
ture, the initial cooling rate would have been r
times more rapid than the present rate, and v
cooling would have taken place during the f
years. No observable cooling is expected tod
thermal state of the planet a few millennia in

It is possible to reconstruct by some simpl
proximately what the thermal history of Venus
like if it had a temperature of about 2000°
years ago. For this calculation, I adopt an ave
ductivity (κ) of rock of about 10^{-2} cal cm^{-1}
sume that radiative cooling to space takes p
boundary of the slowly cooling surface. The
the solid crust after an elapsed time (Δt) is a

$$\Delta x = \sqrt{\frac{\kappa}{\rho c}}\sqrt{\Delta t} = \frac{\sqrt{\Delta t}}{10}$$

For $\Delta t = 3{,}000$ years $= 10^{11}$ sec, this thic
10^4 cm, or about a quarter of a mile. The he
surface at present would be given by:

Heat flux $\simeq \kappa(\Delta T/\Delta x)$

This flux is 10^{-4} cal cm^{-2} sec^{-1}, which is a
flux measured today in the Earth's crust.
than a tenth of the heating that results fro
the surface of Earth, or the upper atmosph
absence of a massive atmosphere to hold t
would yield a surface temperature on Ver

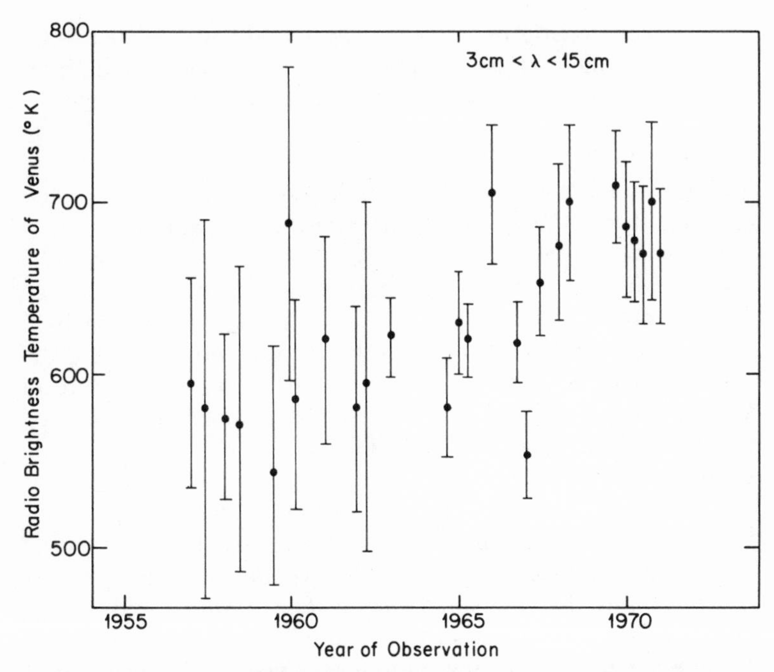

Figure 1. Microwave brightness temperatures of Venus as a function of time. Only observations at wavelengths between 3 and 15 cm are included, since at shorter wavelengths the emission arises in the atmosphere rather than on the surface, while at longer wavelengths the calibration is less secure. The error bars are the uncertainties as estimated by the individual experimenters. The data are from the summaries by A. M. Barrett and D. H. Staelin (*Space Sci. Rev.* 3:109, 1964) and by W. W. Warnock and J. R. Dickel (*Icarus* 17:682, 1972).

past two decades that directly measure *surface* temperature on Venus. These are presented graphically in Figure 1. Clearly, there is no evidence of cooling; on the contrary, the data taken at face value suggest a *warming* of the planet. Again, however, there are calibration problems that mask any possible long-term trends. There is thus no evidence of variation of the surface temperature of Venus, nor are present-day techniques capable of detecting changes of less than 25 degrees at best. Claims that an observed cooling of Venus supports Velikovsky's theory involve both a misunderstanding of the measurements and an erroneous inference that observable cooling would be expected.

DIURNAL VARIATIONS IN TEMPERATURE

A persistent theme in recent pro-Velikovsky writing has been an attempt to discredit explanations of the high surface temperature of Venus based on solar heating and an atmospheric greenhouse effect. One of the arguments concerns the absence of variations in surface temperature from day to night, which was first demonstrated in about 1969 from three sets of radio observations that indicated no variation of the temperature of Venus with phase.[27] In effect, these observations demonstrated for the surface what had been known decades earlier for the cloud tops—that the temperature did not depend on time of day.

It will be remembered that it was the nonvariation of cloud-top temperatures that apparently led Velikovsky first to hypothesize an internal heat source on Venus. He neglected the alternative possibility that the constancy of temperature could be due to the massive heat capacity of a thick atmosphere. His was perhaps an understandable omission, since the atmosphere of Venus was thought twenty-five years ago to be Earth-like. But no such excuse exists for his supporters today, who are well aware of the 100-atmosphere surface pressure on the planet.

The chain of logic on the question of surface temperature variations is virtually the opposite of that published in defense of Velikovsky. A large greenhouse effect can only be maintained by a massive atmosphere, and a massive atmosphere must damp out surface temperature variations. Therefore the absence of such variations is expected where a large greenhouse effect exists. The reason the radio observers (and I was one of them) expressed some surprise at the lack of variation seen in their data was that there were previous suggestions in the literature that this "microwave phase effect" had been detected, not because their results contradicted some preconception based on a greenhouse model. The radio data provide a very weak rod indeed with which to beat greenhouse explanations of the temperature of Venus.

A COUP DE GRACE TO INTERNAL HEAT?

It is clear from thermal history calculations such as the one given above in the section on Maximum Cooling Rate that the maximum internal energy source on Venus should be small. However, any calculation of this sort is model-dependent, and we can never be sure that the model builders have really considered all of the possibilities. Nature sometimes finds ways to accomplish feats that mystify the theoretician. It is much more satisfying to learn that direct, model-independent information exists to demonstrate that internal heat cannot contribute significantly to the surface temperature of Venus.

During the past few years a variety of radar observations have begun to reveal the surface topography of Venus, long hidden beneath her massive atmosphere and thick clouds.[28] The radar images show craters, mountains, and valleys with total vertical relief of several kilometers. Such differences in elevation require a substantial crustal strength for their support. It can be shown that a crust of the requisite thickness of about 10 km cannot conduct enough heat from the interior to make a significant impact on the surface temperature. This thickness is still too great to be accounted for from only a few millennia of cooling, however, as required by Velikovsky's thesis.

Calculations, based on a maximum conductivity and the minimum crusted thickness necessary to support the observed relief, yield a *maximum* energy flux of 6×10^{-6} cal cm^{-2} sec^{-1} reaching the surface.[29] To judge the importance of this energy input relative to that provided by sunlight, we turn to the direct measurements of brightness at the surface made by the Venera 8 lander in 1973. Averaged over the surface, this heat flux from sunlight is 1×10^{-4} cal cm^{-2} sec^{-1}, more than ten times greater than the maximum internal heat flux. Thus, independent of the past history of Venus or its present internal temperature, it can be asserted with confidence that sunlight, rather than internal heat, is the dominant source of energy to the Venerian surface and lower atmosphere. It follows, therefore, that the high surface temperature must result from atmospheric trapping of this heat (the greenhouse effect) and cannot be due to a massive heat flux from the interior as Velikovsky continues to claim.

I have dealt at length with the temperature of Venus, because arguments are so often made that Velikovsky's greatest triumphs have taken place in this arena. The facts are that his claims on the source of heat and the thermal evolution of the planet are inconsistent with even simple physical models, and that current data convincingly show that the high surface temperature has nothing to do with Velikovsky's catastrophist theories.

In summary, none of the thermal predictions for Venus, Mars, or the moon made by Velikovsky has been verified. On the other hand, it is clear that these predictions are not crucial to his theory. Indeed, most were spurious, in that no matter what their state of incandescence several millennia ago might have been, neither Mars nor Venus can be expected to show either excess thermal radiation or progressive cooling of sufficient magnitude to be measurable by existing astronomical techniques. The absence of evidence of major recent lunar heating is more important, but on this object (the moon) the most significant results for Velikovsky's theory relate to the surface features and their ages, not to thermal studies.

The Surfaces of the Moon and Planets

I now turn to the consequences of catastrophic encounters among planets for their surface land forms and morphology and for the dating of these features. Velikovsky suggests that planetary encounters produced massive meteoric bombardment, volcanism, and widespread surface melting on Venus, Mars, the moon, and to perhaps a lesser extent on Earth. The Earth is not my subject in this paper, but I note that one has only to consider the extreme rarity of major terrestrial impact scars[30] to conclude that there has been no recent period of major impacts and cratering. But what of the other planets?

The surfaces of each of the terrestrial planets, except the Earth, have been affected dramatically by collisions with other bodies, as is evident from the numerous impact craters that dominate their topography. Mercury, the moon, and Mars have been extensively studied from spacecraft during the past decade, and the large land forms on Venus have been delineated by radar. Widespread lava flows have occurred on Mercury, the moon, and Mars, but the presence of numerous impact craters on these lava plains shows that they are old, relative to the time scale for meteoric or cometary collisions. In addition, Mars has huge volcanic mountains and associated evidence of tectonic activity, including extensive faulting and the development of a major rift valley system. We do not know whether there are lava flows or volcanoes on Venus.

The radar-revealed craters of Venus are a particular problem for any theory that proposes a recent origin for this planet. We know that at present rates of bombardment of Venus by meteoroids and comets it would require more than a billion years to achieve the observed density of craters. If Venus is only a few thousand years old, these impacts must have occurred at an extraordinarily high rate, and therefore they must have been due to debris associated with the birth of Venus or its subsequent planetary encounters. There is a crucial objection to such a hypothesis, however, for Velikovsky has stated that in those times Venus was incandescent, in which case its surface was molten or at least very plastic, and no permanent craters can have been formed by impacts. In fact, in Velikovsky's scenario, the crust even today would probably be too thin to support these large craters permanently, as noted in the previous section. Only a truly bizarre set of circumstances (added to Velikovsky's already bizarre scenario for Venus) can have allowed all of this debris to survive in the vicinity of Venus until the planet cooled and then to have been swept up to form the observed craters, leaving no satellites or cloud of debris near Venus today. Thus the crater-covered surface of Venus provides one of the strongest arguments against a recent birth for this planet.

The similarity in the major features of the observed surface geology of the terrestrial planets (including the moon) can be understood on the basis of a theory that supposes that the areas of heaviest cratering were formed in the final stages of accretion of the planets from the solar nebula, and that only relatively mild internal activity has taken place since on Mercury and the moon, with greater activity on the larger Mars, and of course vastly greater activity on the still larger Earth. The recent Mariner 10 photos, by revealing that the surface of Mercury is as saturated with craters as are the lunar highlands, has been particularly constructive in clarifying this picture of the basic evolution of the terrestrial planets.[31] It is possible from examination of the detailed photographs now available to construct preliminary geologic maps in which *relative* ages of many features can be deduced from the stratigraphic record. However, it is not possible from remote investigations to establish *absolute* ages. Thus, while these data are consistent with an end to episodes of major cratering about 4×10^9 years ago (not too different from the derived crystallization ages of the oldest terrestrial rocks and of the meteorites), one can not exclude the possibility of a much more recent scenario of cratering. It is therefore important to obtain an estimate of *absolute* ages for some of these features before using the observations of planetary topography to judge whether recent catastrophic encounters are possible.

Fortunately, we do have age estimates for many lunar geologic events in the samples returned to Earth as part of the Apollo and Luna programs. But before discussing these, I note a very simple qualitative argument for the antiquity of the crater-covered surfaces of the moon, Venus, and Mars. As noted above, there are no recent major impact craters on Earth, and from this fact alone one can argue conclusively that the impact craters on these other planets, if they were formed in the vicinity of the Earth, cannot be recent either. There is simply no way that the moon, Mars, and Venus could have been bombarded extensively while near the more massive Earth without our planet also being affected. And no sophisticated dating schemes are required to see the absence of recent craters on the Earth—one has only to use one's eyes.

Quantitative dating of lunar rocks and soils supports this qualitative conclusion. A number of techniques are available. Most involve the determination of the time elapsed since crystallization of a rock from the molten state, a quantity that can be derived from the amounts in the sample of the parent-daughter elements involved in radioactive decay—primarily uranium-thorium-lead, potassium-argon, and rubidium-strontium.[32] These dating methods show that on the moon most rocks excavated by impact cratering are about 4×10^9 years old, and that the last major lava flows took place slightly more than 3×10^9 years ago.[33]

The numbers quoted above for typical crystallization ages of lunar rocks are, of course, subject to some uncertainty. Experimental uncertainties are generally less than 5 percent in the ages, and the results obtained by different investigators using different methods agree to within this level of accuracy. Anderson and Spangler[34] have recently raised the interesting point of possible variations in the decay constant, but their results (if confirmed), while of great theoretical significance, are unlikely to upset greatly these age determinations. Similarly, the many problems associated with carbon-14 dating of archeological materials that are often discussed by Velikovsky's supporters are not relevant to the dating of the crystallization of rocks. Thus, even if one wishes to question the exact dates assigned to lunar materials, their great antiquity relative to the history of humanity is not at issue. Speaking to nearest order of magnitude only, the lunar surface last experienced major melting a *million* times longer ago in the past than the catastrophes suggested by Velikovsky.

Other ways of estimating the age of lunar surface features also exist. In the previous section I noted the absence, from Apollo heat flow and seismic measures, of indications of any recent whole-body heating of the moon, and the corresponding evidence that the crust has been solid for many millions of years. The great age of the crust can also be inferred, qualitatively, from the presence of a regolith of shattered and broken rock many meters thick. It requires a very long time since the crust was last molten to crush and stir that much rock by meteoric impacts. A third line of argument can be developed from the cosmic-ray-exposure ages of the lunar samples. These ages measure the length of time a sample has lain on the lunar surface, where it would have been subject to bombardment by cosmic rays which leave tiny tracks in the minerals. Measured ages vary according to the length of time since a particular rock was excavated and thrown onto the surface, but the ages are (on the assumption of a uniform cosmic-ray-exposure rate) generally many millions of years. Thus, there are three additional ways of setting approximate lower limits on the time since the lunar crust was last melted, and they *all* contradict Velikovsky's theory of a molten, bubbling moon just a few millennia ago.[35]

The above discussion is directed to a crucial issue for the evaluation of Velikovsky in the light of modern planetary astronomy—that of the antiquity of the lunar surface, that is, of the time since there was any significant melting or burst of impacts on the moon. But there are several other peripheral issues in which predictions by Velikovsky[36] can be evaluated in terms of recent lunar data, and these will be discussed very briefly below.

In advance of the first *in situ* measurements, Velikovsky predicted remanent magnetism in the lunar rocks.[37] Some minerals retain evidence of the orientation and strength of the ambient magnetic field at the time their temperatures drop below the Curie point (typically $\sim 1000°K$). The lunar rocks were found to exhibit this phenomenon. However, the crucial point is *when* the rocks were last at temperatures above the Curie point. The remanent magnetism can refer to historical times only if the temperature were fortuitously raised just enough to be above the Curie point but remained too low to melt the rock and thus reset the radioactive clocks. Clearly, the presence of remanent magnetism does not contradict the great antiquity of the moon derived from the crystallization ages of the rocks. Velikovsky does not indicate how strong the magnetic field might have been at the time of his postulated encounters but implies values much higher than we see today on the Earth; it is, therefore, worth noting that the former lunar magnetic field indicated by the remanent magnetism is only a few percent of the present terrestrial field.

One of Velikovsky's most bizarre claims concerns the origins of the lunar craters. He has frequently asserted that the bubbling of the lunar surface when it was recently molten explains many craters; for instance, in 1969 he wrote that "of the lunar ringforming formations a larger number resulted from bubbling activity."[38] Lunar craters have been subject to intense scrutiny by geologists, and I know of no student of the problem during the past fifty years who believes the craters could have been formed by this mechanism, either recently as suggested by Velikovsky, or in the distant past. In fact, a most convincing demonstration that the lunar craters cannot have been formed by bubbles was published in 1921 by Alfred Wegener, the father of continental drift.[39] It is an indication of Velikovsky's unfamiliarity with physical and geological concepts that he seems unaware of these arguments even in the mid-1970's.[40]

Before the first lunar landing, Velikovsky warned that lightninglike electric discharges between the moon and other bodies could have produced high levels of radioactivity on the lunar surface. In 1967 he wrote that "radioactivity must still be present on the surface of the Moon in quantity damaging to unprotected man or animal and by far exceeding any exposure regarded as safe."[41] Subsequently, radioactivity in the lunar crust has been studied in the returned samples and through survey programs carried out from lunar orbit, and the results show amounts of radioactive elements (primarily uranium, thorium, and potassium) comparable to those in many terrestrial basalts.[42] The lunar surface certainly is not dangerously radioactive; however, I fail to see this result as relevant to Velikovsky's theory, because the whole idea that interplanetary lightning bolts should cause radioactivity is without foundation.

In this section we have seen several lines of evidence that show that the surface of the moon is old, and that neither Earth nor the moon has recently been subject to major recent cratering or melting. The antiquity of the lunar volcanic and impact features is fundamentally in conflict with the catastrophic interplanetary encounters proposed by Velikovsky. So also is the presence of a cratered surface on Venus. Several of the other arguments discussed in this paper represent side issues, but *in these areas the astronomical evidence flatly contradicts fundamental aspects of Velikovsky's theory.*

Conclusions

In this chapter I have endeavored to review nearly all of the astronomically testable predictions made in *Worlds in Collision* and in subsequent publications by Velikovsky. I have tried to avoid the pitfalls associated with discussion of isolated phenomena, but have rather attempted to present a broad picture that calls attention to as many as possible of the important areas in which modern observations of the moon and planets relate to Velikovsky's theories.

The reader will note that, in spite of my effort to present a comprehensive picture, fewer than a score of specific astronomical consequences of planetary encounters have been discussed. Most of these predictions were first published twenty-five years ago. I do not apologize for concentrating attention on the contents of *Worlds in Collision,* since Velikovsky has stated as recently as his lecture at the 1974 AAAS meeting that he stood by his original book and that he knew of no case where his predictions had subsequently been shown to be incorrect.[43] I submit that while most of the evidence discussed here is inconclusive, *there is not one fundamental or crucial prediction that has been confirmed, whereas several basic points are now clearly seen to be incorrect.* Research on the planets has shown the chemical dissimilarity between Venus and Jupiter, the absence of any indications of exchange of atmospheres among Venus, Mars, and Earth, and, most importantly, the impressive accumulation of evidence against recent periods of major thermal, volcanic, or impact catastrophes on the moon or the terrestrial planets. It is difficult for anyone with training in the physical sciences to understand how Velikovsky's ideas, after such a consistent record of failures, can continue to attract wide public interest and generate ardent defenders.

From an astronomical perspective, the past quarter-century of planetary exploration has repeatedly contradicted Velikovsky's catastrophic theories. This period has witnessed an extraordinary advance in understanding the physical nature of the planets, due largely to direct investigation by spacecraft and to the many ground-based observations carried on in support of the space program. Many of the questions raised in *Worlds in Collision* concerning the physics and chemistry of Venus, Mars, and the moon have now been conclusively answered, and, as reviewed here, the facts are almost entirely inconsistent with Velikovsky's expectations. Certainly, there is no compelling astronomical evidence in favor of Velikovsky; quite the contrary, a great deal that seemed plausible or at least possible in 1950 has since been shown to be incorrect. One must look to fields other than astronomy for evidence in favor of recent planetary catastrophism, and even if such evidence is found, it would be wise to keep in mind the virtual impossibility of reconciling such events with the astronomical evidence now available.

Acknowledgments

I am indebted to Carl Sagan for pointing out to me the argument presented here for dealing with the formation of the Venerian craters, to Ralph E. Juergens for pointing out the significance of the presence of a deep lunar regolith, and to Sagan for the explanation of the genesis of the story that Mariner 2 had detected hydrocarbon clouds on Venus. I also acknowledge the criticisms of six referees who vigorously attacked all weak arguments in the original version of this chapter when it was submitted for publication in *Pensée*, and to further criticism of the present manuscript by Clark R. Chapman.

Notes

1. I. Velikovsky, *Worlds in Collision* (New York: Doubleday, 1950). Otherwise unattributed references to Velikovsky in this chapter are to this book.
2. For an extensive, albeit frequently incorrect, summary of this supposed evidence see "A Record of Success" by T. Ferté, *Pensée* 2, No. 2: 16, 1972.
3. I. Michelson, *Pensée* 4, No. 2: 15, 1974; also a paper given at the McMas-

ter University symposium on "Velikovsky and the Recent History of the Solar System," June, 1974 (unpublished manuscript).

4. Velikovsky made the prediction that Jupiter would be a radio source in his "Forum Address" of October 14, 1953; it is printed as an appendix to *Earth in Upheaval* (New York: Doubleday, 1955). This prediction was extensively reviewed in the context of what was known in 1953 about the origin of cosmic radio radiation by J. Warwick at the McMaster University symposium in June, 1974 (unpublished manuscript).

5. For example: W. B. Hubbard, *Astrophys. J.* 155:333, 1969; W. B. Hubbard, *Astrophys. J.* 162:687, 1970; W. B. Hubbard, *Icarus* 21:157, 1974; R. Smoluchowski, in T. Gehrels, ed., *Jupiter* (Tucson: University of Arizona Press, 1976), p. 3; V. N. Zharkov and V. P. Trubitsyn, *ibid*, p. 133.

6. J. S. Lewis, "Earth and Planet." *Sci. Lett.* 15:286, 1972; see also J. S. Lewis, *Sci. American* 230, No. 3:50, 1974.

7. S. T. Ridgway, *Astrophys. J.* 187:L41, 1974; R. G. Prinn and T. Owen, in T. Gehrels, ed., *Jupiter* (Tucson: University of Arizona Press, 1976), 319; S. T. Ridgway, H. P. Larson, and U. Fink, *ibid*, p. 384.

8. Good reviews of the structure and chemistry of the Venerian atmosphere are provided by M. Ya. Marov, *Icarus* 16:415, 1972; A. T. Young, *Icarus* 18:564, 1973; M. J. S. Belton, in J. E. Hansen, ed., *The Atmosphere of Venus* (NASA SP-382, 1975), p. 114.

9. A. T. Young, *Icarus* 18:564, 1973; G. T. Sill, *Comm. Lunar Planet. Lab.* 9:191, 1972; J. V. Martonchik, *Astrophys. J.* 193:495, 1974.

10. F. C. Gillett et al., *J. Atmos. Sci.* 25:594, 1968; J. Connes et al., *Atlas des spectres dans le proche infrarouge de Venus, Mars, Jupiter, et Saturne* (Paris: Editions du Centre National de la Récherche Scientifique, 1969); W. T. Plummer, *Science* 163:1191, 1969 (reprinted in *Pensée* 4, No. 1:20, 1973–1974); T. Owen and C. Sagan, *Icarus* 16:557, 1972; W. A. Burgstahler, *Pensée* 4, No. 1:24, 1973–1974; J. B. Pollack et al., *Icarus* 23:8, 1974.

11. See p. 76 above for Sagan's version of this misunderstanding. Unfortunately, this hypothesis is still occasionally quoted in popular articles.

12. In a letter to H. Hess dated August 7, 1969 (*Pensée* 2, No. 3:29, 1972), Velikovsky specifically stated "I claimed that neon and argon are the *chief* constituents of the Martian atmosphere" (emphasis added).

13. G. Neugebauer et al., *Science* 166:98, 1969; and *Astron. J.* 76:719, 1971; K. C. Herr and G. C. Pimentel, *Science* 166:496, 1969. The Mariner 9 results are presented in a series of papers published in the October, 1972, issue of *Icarus* and in the July 10, 1973, issue of the *J. Geophys. Res.* Viking results are in the December 17, 1976, issue of *Science*.

14. T. Owen and C. Sagan, *Icarus* 16:557, 1972.

15. By the early 1970's it was generally felt that well over 90 percent of the Martian atmosphere was probably carbon dioxide; e.g., see D. M. Hunten, *Space Sci. Rev.* 12:539, 1971. However, the situation was complicated in 1974 when the U.S.S.R. spacecraft Mars 6 made measurements during descent through the Martian atmosphere (the craft then failed upon touchdown) that suggested tens of percent of argon might be present. See V. G. Istomin and K. V. Grechnev, *Icarus* 28:155, 1976; V. I. Moroz, *Icarus* 28:159, 1976. Although highly ambiguous, these Russian results greatly heightened interest in the Viking mea-

surements of the quantity of argon. As it turned out, the Russians were wrong and the pre-1974 analyses had been correct.

16. T. Owen and K. Biemann, *Science* 193:801, 1976; also other related Viking papers in *Science* for August 27, October 1, and December 17, 1976.

17. H. H. Kieffer et al., *J. Geophys. Res.* 78:4291, 1973; H. H. Kieffer et al., *Science* 193:780, 1976.

18. E. Pettit, in G. P. Kuiper and B. M. Middlehurst, eds., *Planets and Satellites* (Chicago: U. of Chicago Press, 1961), p. 400.

19. Letter from Velikovsky to H. Hess, July 2, 1964, published in *Pensée* 2, No. 3:29, 1972; also *New York Times,* July 21, 1969, early city edition, p. 13.

20. M. G. Langseth et al., *Proc. 7th Lunar Sci. Conf.* (1976), p. 3143; note that this is a revision downward of earlier Apollo values.

21. For example: W. M. Sinton and J. Strong, *Astrophys. J.* 131:470, 1960; S. C. Chase, L. D. Kaplan, and G. Neugebauer, *Science* 139:907, 1963; B. C. Murray, R. L. Wildey, and J. A. Westphal, *J. Geophys. Res.* 68:4813, 1963; J. B. Pollack and C. Sagan, *J. Geophys. Res.* 70:4403, 1965; R. Goody, *J. Geophys. Res.* 70:5471, 1965; M. Ya. Marov, *Icarus* 16:415, 1972; S. C. Chase et al., *Science* 183:1291, 1974.

22. For reviews of the microwave data see: A. M. Barrett and D. H. Staelin, *Space Sci. Rev.* 3:109, 1964; J. B. Pollack and D. Morrison, *Icarus* 12:376, 1970; C. Sagan, in C. Sagan et al., eds., *Planetary Atmospheres* (Dordrecht, Holland: Reidel, 1971), p. 116; W. W. Warnock and J. R. Dickel, *Icarus* 17:682, 1972. The Venera 7 results are reported by V. S. Avduevsky et al., *J. Atmos. Sci.* 28:269, 1971.

23. M. Ya. Marov et al., *Icarus* 20:407, 1973.

24. I. Velikovsky, *Pensée* 2, No. 2:51, 1972. This "test" was also discussed by Velikovsky in *Yale Sci. Mag.* 41 (1967) and *Pensée* 4, No. 1:21, 1973–1974.

25. See note 21 above.

26. See note 9 above.

27. J. R. Dickel et al., *Nature* 220:1183, 1968; D. Morrison, *Science* 163:815, 1969; T. P. McCullough, *Icarus* 16:310, 1972.

28. D. B. Campbell et al., *Science* 175:514, 1972; G. H. Pettengill et al., *Bull. American Astron. Soc.* 5:302, 1973; A. E. E. Rogers et al., *Astron. J.* 77:100, 1972.

29. D. Morrison, *Icarus* 28:423, 1976.

30. Fewer than 50 major impact craters have been identified on Earth, most so degraded by erosion and deposition that they have only recently been recognized from large-scale aerial and satellite photographs.

31. See, for instance: B. C. Murray et al., *J. Geophys Res.* 80:2508, 1975; W. M. Kaula, *Icarus* 26:1, 1975.

32. There is by now a massive literature on dating of lunar rocks. Ten easily accessible technical papers on dating of Apollo 11 samples only are in *Science* for January 30, 1970. A recent summary of all Apollo dates is by F. Tera, D. A. Papanastassiou, and G. J. Wasserburg, in *Lunar Sci. IV* (Houston: NASA Lunar Science Inst., 1973), p. 723. See also the discussions in S. R. Taylor, *Lunar Science: A Post-Apollo View* (New York: Pergamon Press, 1975).

33. It is perhaps worth noting that these radio-dating techniques are rather more sophisticated than is indicated in some popular accounts, in that by mea-

suring the concentrations of a variety of isotopes (both radiogenic and natural) of identical chemical properties and volatility it is possible to deduce the age without knowing the original parent-daughter ratios, and in many cases it is also possible to identify and correct for possible postcrystallization environmental effects, such as heating or impact shocking.

34. J. L. Anderson and G. W. Spangler, *Pensée* 4, No. 4:31, 1974.

35. Velikovsky has repeatedly stressed that his theory predicts large-scale lunar melting. Thus, in a March 14, 1967 memorandum: "Of the many craters on the Moon, some—with raised rims and with no rills radiating from them—were in my understanding formed while, in cosmic disturbances, the surface of the Moon became molten and boiled" (*Pensée* 2, No. 3:28, 1972). In a May 19, 1969 memorandum: "The Moon was repeatedly heated and its entire surface melted less than 35 and 27 centuries ago" (*ibid,* p. 29). In the *New York Times* for July 21, 1969: "I maintain that less than 3,000 years ago the Moon's surface was repeatedly molten and its surface bubbled" (see note 19 above).

36. See, for example, note 2 above.

37. See, for instance, *New York Times* article (see note 19 above).

38. Memo to H. Hess, *Pensée* 2, No. 3:29, 1972.

39. A. Wegener, *The Origin of Lunar Craters* (Braunschweig: Friedrich Vieweg und Sohn, 1921), p. 41; English translation in *The Moon* 14:211, 1972.

40. The small bubbles throughout the lunar rocks are, of course, evidence of a former molten state; in this respect the lunar lavas are similar to their terrestrial counterparts. As noted above, however, the lunar lavas appear to have cooled several billion years ago.

41. Memo to H. Hess, *Pensée* 2, No. 3:28, 1972.

42. D. L. Anderson and T. C. Hanks, *Science* 178:1245, 1972; A. E. Metzger et al., *Science* 179:800, 1973.

43. *Pensée* 4, No. 2:10, 1974.

Contributors

DONALD GOLDSMITH, author of *The Universe,* was Assistant Professor of Astronomy at the State University of New York, Stony Brook, before assuming his present position as President of Interstellar Media.

NORMAN W. STORER, author of *Focus on Society: An Introduction to Sociology,* is Professor of Sociology, Baruch College, City University of New York.

CARL SAGAN is David Duncan Professor of Astronomy and Space Sciences and Director of the Laboratory for Planetary Studies at Cornell University. He is co-editor with Thornton Page of *UFO's—A Scientific Debate,* and author of *The Cosmic Connection* and *The Dragons of Eden: Speculation on the Evolution of Human Intelligence.*

J. DERRAL MULHOLLAND is a research scientist in the Department of Astronomy, University of Texas.

PETER J. HUBER is Professor of Mathematical Statistics, Eidgenössische Technische Hochschule, Zurich.

DAVID MORRISON is Assistant Deputy Director, Lunar and Planetary Programs, NASA Headquarters, Washington, D.C., and a staff member of the Institute for Astronomy, University of Hawaii.

Bibliography

Asimov, Isaac. "Worlds in Confusion," *Fantasy and Science Fiction,* October, 1969.

——. "CP," *Analog Science Fiction,* October, 1974.

de Camp, L. Sprague. *Lost Continents* (New York: Dover Books, 1970; reprinted, Ballantine Books, 1975).

de Grazia, Alfred, ed. *The Velikovsky Affair* (New Hyde Park: University Books, 1966).

Gardner, Martin. *Fads and Fallacies in the Name of Science* (New York: Dover Books, 1957).

Menzel, Donald, "The Celestial Mechanics of Electrically Charged Planets," *Proceedings of the American Philosophical Society 96:* 524, 1952.

North, John. "Venus, by Jupiter!" *Times Literary Supplement,* June 25, 1976, p. 770.

Payne-Gaposchkin, Cecilia. "Worlds in Collision," *Proceedings of the American Philosophical Society 96:* 519, 1952.

Pensée (ten issues devoted to Immanuel Velikovsky; Portland, Oregon: 1972–1974).

Velikovsky, Immanuel. "Cosmos without Gravitation," Scientific Report IV of the *Scripta Academica Hierosolymitana* (New York-Jerusalem: Simon Velikovsky Foundation, 1946).

——. *Worlds in Collision* (New York: Doubleday, 1950; Dell Books, 1967).

——. *Earth in Upheaval* (New York: Doubleday, 1955; Dell Books, 1968).

——. *Ages in Chaos* (New York: Doubleday, 1952; Dell Books, 1968).

——. *Oedipus and Akhnaton: Myth and History* (New York: Doubleday, 1960).

——. *Peoples of the Sea* (New York: Doubleday, 1977).

Velikovsky Reconsidered, by the Editors of *Pensée* (New York: Doubleday, 1976).

Vitaliano, Dorothy B. *Legends of the Earth: Their Geologic Origins* (Bloomington, Ind.: Indiana University Press, 1973).

Index

Scientists Confront Velikovsky

Designed by R. E. Rosenbaum.
Composed by Vail-Ballou Press, Inc.,
in 10 point VIP Primer, 2 points leaded,
with display lines in Primer.
Printed offset by Vail-Ballou Press on
Warren's No. 66 text, 50 pound basis.
Bound by Vail-Ballou Press
in GSB book cloth
and stamped in All Purpose foil.

Library of Congress Cataloging in Publication Data
(For library cataloging purposes only)

Main entry under title:
Scientists confront Velikovsky.

Bibliography: p.
Includes index.
1. Velikovsky, Immanuel, 1895- 2. Astronomy—History. I. Goldsmith, Donald.
QB32.S34 1977 001.9'092'4 77-2457
ISBN 0-8014-0961-6